THE
ILLUSTRATED ENCYCLOPAEDIA
OF ANIMAL LIFE

THE ANIMAL KINGDOM

The strange and wonderful ways of
mammals, birds, reptiles, fishes and
insects. A new and authentic natural
history of the wild life of the world

VOLUME 6

FREDERICK DRIMMER, M.A.
EDITOR-IN-CHIEF

GEORGE G. GOODWIN
Associate Curator of Mammals,
The American Museum of Natural
History

DEAN AMADON
E. THOMAS GILLIARD
Associate Curators of Birds,
The American Museum of Natural History

CHARLES M. BOGERT
Curator of Amphibians and Reptiles,
The American Museum of Natural
History

CHRISTOPHER W. COATES *Curator*
JAMES W. ATZ *Assistant Curator*
Aquarium of the New York Zoological
Society

JOHN C. PALLISTER
Research Associate, Insects, The American Museum of Natural History

LEOPARD SEALS—THEY EAT THEIR OWN KIND

The Leopard Seal, *Hydrurga leptonyx*, is among the best known of the Antarctic seals. A ferocious creature, it preys on other seals as well as fish. Many seals have teeth that are mere pegs for catching and holding fish—not so the leopard seal, which is equipped with large molars well adapted for rending and tearing the flesh of the animals devoured by this carnivorous finfoot.

The leopard seal is large—males reach a length of ten to twelve feet, females are about seven feet long. The coarse coat of yellowish-grey hair is dappled with numerous black spots and sometimes with light blotches on the back.

ELEPHANT SEALS—BIGGEST OF THEIR TRIBE

The Elephant Seal, *Mirounga*, is not only the largest of the seals but also the ugliest and clumsiest. Its name is derived from its enormous size—also from the peculiar, apparently useless, elongated snout of cavernous tissue. In the relaxed state this appendage hangs eight or nine inches below the mouth. When a bull utters its deep, ventril-

A SEAL WITH A STRANGE-LOOKING NOSE

The name "elephant seal" accurately describes this largest of all seals, which can weigh more than five thousand pounds. Its long nose, faintly similar to the elephant's trunk, is made of tissue which hangs slackly down over the animal's mouth when it is quiet. When the seal roars, this queer projection blows up with air. An unusually thick layer of blubber under the elephant seal's hide causes it to quiver like a mass of gelatine when the animal shuffles along. This seal was formerly slain in great numbers for its fat and oil.

oquial roar, this snout swells up with air and the tip curls into the seal's mouth.

Large males reach a length of eighteen or twenty feet, weighing a fantastic five thousand pounds or more. The females are about ten feet long. When one of these ponderous and grotesque leviathans is on shore, its huge body settles into an almost formless heap, its coarse skin wrinkled, furrowed, and cracked. When the time comes to shed the bleached brown coat, the cuticle peels off in large blisters along with the hair, looking as if it had been severely burned by the sun.

The elephant seal has very simple tastes—it lives to sleep and eat. Let a rude jolt break its slumber and its mighty front flipper drives a stinging shower of sand and small stones—very accurately, by the way—at the cause of the disturbance. This done, the seal promptly goes back to sleep.

In the water the elephant seal moves gracefully and rhythmically, and is capable of cruising along at a fair speed. It descends to considerable depths to feed, consuming slow-moving fishes—ratfish, dogfish, and the like—as well as small sharks and squids. The sea elephant's stomach, like a bird's crop, contains a quantity of stones and pebbles that apparently mill the food for digestion.

The breeding pattern is much the same as among the other seals. The males come ashore about the middle of August, and some time later they select their harems from among the newly arriving females. There follows the characteristic brawling and commotion for the rest of the breeding season. Some time between February and June the female gives birth to one black pup on the beach, some distance away from the main herd.

The elephant seal has been killed for its fat and oil for many generations. Formerly the herds numbered in the thousands; today they have become so scarce that commercial hunting is no longer profitable.

The Northern Sea Elephant, reduced to a few individuals on Guadalupe Island off Baja California, was saved from extinction by the Mexican government in 1911. A garrison was posted on the island with orders to shoot poachers and other molesters of the herds. Formerly found on islands of the South Atlantic, South Pacific, Indian, and Antarctic Oceans, this seal has few if any survivors.

The Southern Elephant Seal is responding to protection on Campbell

Island, three hundred miles south of New Zealand; but, like its northern cousin, this species has become all but extinct.

SOME OTHER INTERESTING SEALS

The Ribbon Seal, a rare variety that dwells along the coasts of Alaska, the Aleutian Islands, and the Kurile Islands, is the most ornately marked of the seal tribe. It is highly prized by the Eskimos. The Crab-eating Seal of the Antarctic ice-packs is a much larger animal

ALMOST LIKE A FISH OUT OF WATER

Superlative swimmers, the true seals are but barely able to walk on land. Their hind limbs are flippers, which extend backward instead of rotating forward, as in the eared seals; their front limbs are like paddles. When the true seal walks, its hind flippers and tail are raised above the ground. It propels its body forward by contracting its muscles and using its front paddles. Pictured here is the ribbon seal of Alaska, an unusual and beautifully striped animal.

with an interesting peculiarity—it has lobes in its teeth. Water passes out of the lobes when the jaws are closed, but crustaceans cannot pass through these strainers; thus the victims are held back and swallowed. The Ross Seal, another Antarctic denizen, is small and seldom encountered. Much more common is Weddell's Seal, which lives in the same region.

The Monk Seal favours warm climates—we find it in the Mediterranean, the Caribbean, and in the Pacific, in the neighbourhood of the Hawaiian Islands and Midway Island. The Hooded Seal, on the other hand, prefers pretty much the same surroundings as the harp seal—the ice-floes of the North Atlantic and Arctic waters. The "hood" is an inflatable bag of muscular tissue extending from the muzzle over the top of the head. Only the males have this feature. When they are excited, especially during the mating season, the bladder swells up, giving them a most sinister appearance. The males fight savagely during the mating season, and the roars of the spring battles can be heard at a great distance.

Sea Cows, Manatees, and Dugongs— Sirens But Not Seductive

IF YOU have ever seen these massive, grotesque creatures, you can relish how fantastically inappropriate it would be to call them "sirens". Yet sirens they used to be called—even the scientists gravely endorsed the use of this incongruous name by placing these unromantic animals in the order Sirenia.

How did this come about? Centuries ago, when the animal kingdom was by no means so thoroughly explored as it is today, sailors returning from the Red Sea and Indian Ocean brought back tales of flying fishes, of gold, pearls, precious stones—and strange creatures.

What kind of strange creatures? Well, they were supposed to be half fish and half human, and they were glimpsed frolicking about close to land. To the sailors, at first they suggested mermaids. It was a faintly plausible illusion to at least this extent, that a female dugong carries her baby in her arms and nurses it at her breast in much the same way that a human mother does.

The Japanese capitalized on the tradition. There was a "factory" in Japan which prepared so-called stuffed "mermaids" that were sold as the real thing. The famous Fejee Mermaid, which Barnum exhibited at his Museum in America in 1842, very likely originated in Japan. As thousands flocked to see this hoax, the great showman's gate receipts swelled mightily.

The sirenians, timid animals with a vegetarian diet, are adapted for life in the water. They never leave it—not even to breed. On land they would be completely helpless, unable to propel themselves or to secure food. Scientists conjecture that the sirenians—like the whales in similar straits—might even collapse their lungs by the sheer weight of their bodies.

Sirenians occupy the shallower waters between the deep sea and dry land, frequenting sheltered harbours, bays, lagoons, and estuaries; some even ascend large rivers. In the shallow water they are safe from attack by such raiders of the high seas as the killer whale and shark. We find sirenians in both the Old World and the New; they favour the warmer regions, though in past ages they were not unknown in the Bering Sea.

The sirenians are descended from a long line of water-dwelling ancestors that crawled up on land and then took to the water once more. Scientists tell us that these creatures derive from the ancestral stock whence the elephants and hyraxes originated; however, the relationship is remote.

The sirenians are massive. But they are also spindle shaped, tapering in front to a round head with small eyes and a blunt, sometimes jowly muzzle. The body is rounded in outline and narrows down toward the tail, which in turn flares out horizontally to form a broad, flat paddle. Sirenians have a greyish-coloured skin; some are sparsely bristled all over, others only on the muzzle. We find no trace of hind limbs in present-day sirenians, but they do have paddle-like forelimbs. These animals need to be able to submerge quickly, and their exceptionally dense and heavy bones make this fairly easy.

Sirenians feed on seaweed and other plants which they find in salt and brackish water. As such fodder is none too plentiful, the animals are never very common anywhere. Grazing like cattle, they have no occasion for speed in getting a living. There are two kinds of sirenians in existence, the Dugong (family Dugongidae) and the Manatee (family Trichechidae). The Sea Cow (family Hydrodamalidae) has been extinct for almost two centuries.

DUGONGS—BIG GAME OF THE OCEANS

The Dugong, or Halicore, *Dugong dugon*. The Australian aborigines have an accomplished technique for hunting the dugong. They use a harpoon fitted with a detachable wooden handle, fastened to a line. When the harpoon strikes the dugong, it is anchored by the barbed tip and the shaft floats free except for the attached line. By following the floating shaft, the hunters can trail the dugong until it is tired out —this takes about half an hour. Then the hunters draw their canoe alongside the exhausted quarry and close its nostrils with wooden plugs. Apparently unable to breathe through the mouth, the dugong suffocates.

The dugong is by no means limited to Australian waters. We find it in the warm coastal waters of the East, in the shallow bays and estuaries from the Red Sea to the Indian Ocean, east to the Solomon and Marshall Islands and south to northern Australia.

A full-grown male may reach a length of nine feet; the female is smaller. The dugong's body is covered with blubber and a thick hide —together, they are about an inch in thickness; the hide is hairless except around the mouth. (It is believed, by the way, that the Israelites covered the Ark of the Covenant with skins of the dugong.) The animal's looks are not improved by the downward bend of the jaw that accommodates a pair of incisor teeth developed over the ages into sharp-edged tusks. These continue to grow throughout the life of the dugong. The tail has two lobes, and is rather like a whale's.

While these creatures are not given to living in groups, several may graze in one place on their favoured foods—green seaweed and other water plants. When feeding, the dugong comes up for air every five or ten minutes; the nostrils are opened to take in fresh air but are closed like valves when the animal submerges. Dugongs have poor eyesight, but their hearing is good, despite their lack of an outside ear. The female gives birth to one young at a time, twelve months after mating. She carries the baby about in her flippers.

NORTHERN SEA COWS—GIANTS OF YESTERDAY

The Northern or Steller's Sea Cow, *Hydrodamalis stelleri*, is extinct. It took man until 1741 to discover the sea cow, but from then he needed only twenty-seven years to destroy the entire race. Vitus Bering and George Wilhelm Steller, the naturalist who sailed with him, first found the sea cow on their arrival at Bering Island.

Where Steller's sea cow came from and how it reached its shallow offshore home are among the unfathomed mysteries of bygone ages. The animal was virtually a prisoner, for any attempt to leave the protection of the islands where it dwelled meant certain death; fierce killer whales patrolled the neighbouring waters. The chances are that there were less than fifteen hundred animals in the isolated colony where they were discovered, and that they would have become extinct in the course of time even without man's efficient assistance.

The sea cow, one of the strangest-looking animals of modern times, reached a length of twenty-five or thirty feet and weighed over four tons. It was covered with a rough, coarse hide cracked and wrinkled like the bark of a gnarled old oak tree. It had no teeth; instead, two pairs of grooved, horny plates ground the seaweed on which it fed. Lacking any trace whatever of hind limbs, the sea cow had curiously clublike forelimbs doubled under in the form of a hook. These were used not for swimming but to haul the huge body along in shallow water.

Steller tells us that the sea cows lived cattle-wise in herds offshore. In resting or sleeping, sea cows would roll over on their backs in quiet waters and allow themselves to drift like logs. Occupied with little else but the search for food, they tore seaweed from rocks, and ate incessantly. Yet they apparently had room for the finer feelings: they showed an uncommon solicitude for one another—when one was harpooned, all the rest would try to release it.

MANATEES—TOO PEACEABLE FOR THEIR OWN GOOD

The Manatee, *Trichechus*, is a large, robust, water-dwelling mammal. It averages about seven feet in length and some 450 pounds in weight. Exceptional manatees may measure twelve feet, with an estimated weight of two thousand pounds.

According to native folklore in Mexico, the male manatee sometimes comes ashore on dark nights and carries off the women in the villages along river banks. However, as the manatee is helpless on land, even the natives can hardly take this superstitious notion very seriously.

The people of tropical America have been eating the flesh of the manatee for centuries. It is rich red meat, and is quite palatable. The oil or fat is sweet, and is used by the natives for cooking. At first taken for a fish, the manatee could be eaten on meatless fast days. Later on, religion caught up with science and the manatee disappeared from Friday and Lenten menus.

As for the eating habits of the manatee itself, it is a strict vegetarian, consuming anywhere from sixty to a hundred pounds of seaweed in a single day. Usually it has six teeth on each side of the upper and lower jaws. As worn-out teeth fall out in front, the whole line pushes forward and a new tooth comes in place at the rear.

The manatee has valvelike nostrils; the eyes are small and sunken. Its head is blunt, with thick, pendulous lips. An interesting feature of the upper lip is that it is split lengthwise in two lobes that move independently as the animal feeds. Stubby hairs are scattered over the body, while on the muzzle we find larger stiff bristles. The fore-limbs are modified into broad flippers with rudimentary nails, while the tail is broad, flat, and rounded like a huge paddle.

Fifteen minutes is usually the maximum that a manatee will stay submerged. However, in an emergency an adult can stay down for nearly half an hour. When resting, the manatee floats in the water with its back humped up, the head and tail dangling. In shallow water it curls its tail under, with the upper side resting on the bottom. Breathing normally, the animal has a heart rate of fifty beats a minute, but this is slowed down to thirty in a dive.

Despite its clumsy appearance and expressionless face, the manatee is not quite so stupid as is generally supposed. One manatee in the Miami aquarium frequently offered its right flipper to shake hands, and it would "rub noses" with its keeper. On more than one occasion, a pair of manatees have been seen kissing each other. The manatees are sociable and peaceful in their ways of life; we find very little quarrelling among them. Life, however, is not always tranquil for the manatees in the wild state. There is a constant threat of death in the crocodile-infested waters, while lurking sharks prevent the manatees from escaping to deep waters. If they managed to reach greater depths, they would meet added peril from killer whales. The basic fact of the manatee's existence is that it is not equipped for defence.

We divide the manatees into four species: the African Manatee, found along the west coat from Senegal to the Cuanza River in Angola; the West Indies Manatee, of the Caribbean; the Florida Manatee, dwelling in the coastal waters of eastern North America from North Carolina to Florida and Central America; and Natrerer's Manatee, occurring in the rivers of north-eastern South America. In the northern part of the manatee's range there is some seasonal migration.

ONCE THOUGHT TO BE HALF FISH AND HALF HUMAN

A long time ago the manatee, seen from afar by imaginative sailors, was taken for a "human fish". This mistake probably arose from the fact that the mother manatee looks surprisingly human as she holds her nursing baby to her mammary glands, located on her chest. Although the manatee is a mammal, it lives in the water and cannot move on land. Seen here is the Florida manatee, found in the coastal waters of eastern North America.

MANATEES MAKE GOOD PARENTS

The young, generally one or two, come into the world in April or May and weigh about sixty pounds. Born under water, they are immediately raised to the surface by the mother. Like all mammals, the manatee is a warm-blooded, air-breathing creature that would suffocate if it could not get air. Every three or four minutes, night and day, mother and baby must come to the surface to breathe. The mammary glands are located on the chest, and the pup is clasped in the mother's flippers as it nurses with its head above water.

It is fascinating to watch the manatees taking care of their young. When an 850-pound female gave birth to a forty-pound baby at the Miami aquarium, she took the baby up to air on her shoulder. The male parent was so solicitous of its welfare that when the female did not take it up soon enough to satisfy him, he prodded her with his flukes.

Another birth occurred in a salt-water pool at Windley Key, Florida, after the mother had been kept alone in the pool for 152 days. In this instance, observers saw the cow in shallow water. Suddenly she rolled herself on her side, and when she righted herself the baby was on her back. She kept her offspring in this position out of water for forty-five minutes; then submerged but quickly rose to the surface again. She repeated this action several times, gradually increasing the tempo and the length of time she stayed under water.

Neither the cow nor the calf came to the surface while nursing. Not infrequently the calf linked its flippers through the mother's in a most human manner and they both swam about the pool with linked arms.

As has been suggested, the male manatee is a good husband and a devoted father. A baby manatee born in a zoological park was seen to receive fond care from both its parents; when one parent was ready to relinquish its charge, the other was there to take over. The little fellow's first days of life were spent being tossed back and forth without a chance to swim.

A youngster remains with the parents until it is half grown. Once the offspring are able to get about by themselves, the manatees gather in groups of fifteen or twenty. They are surprisingly active as they sport and play.

Elephants—The World's Largest and Most Powerful Land Animals

MORE THAN any other living creature, the elephant challenges and fires our imaginations. A unique combination of huge size, strange appearance, tremendous power, unexpected gracefulness and smoothly rhythmical action, it is perpetually on the move.

Seeing a herd of these gigantic pachyderms in their native haunts at close range seems to take us back to some faraway geological time, into an eerie and mysterious age when such mighty mammals were the greatest power on the earth.

The Asiatic and two African species of today are all that remain of a once great elephant population that roamed over most of the Northern Hemisphere. Not more than fifteen thousand years ago—only yesterday in geological time!—woolly mammoths were plentiful on the grassy tundra of the polar region of the North. They had gigantic curling tusks and a winter coat of thick hair that almost reached the ground. Some of them, like the Columbia and Imperial mammoths of North America and the straight-tusked varieties of Italy, stood thirteen feet and over at the shoulder. On Cyprus and other Mediterranean islands, on the other hand, there were dwarf elephants no bigger than a pony. Mastodons were common in Europe, Asia, and North America.

There is some evidence, by the way, that early man slew the elephant with his primitive weapons. Later—though still in prehistoric times—man captured the elephant alive and trained the huge creature to do his bidding.

A CLOSE LOOK AT THE ELEPHANT

Elephants are the largest and most powerful land animals alive in the world today. These monsters of the tropical jungles and grassy plains of Asia and Africa are mighty enough to command immunity from attack by any other living wild creature.

The elephant is covered with a thick grey hide, leathery and tough in texture. Though this hide is a good inch thick, an elephant is very sensitive to cold. Even a slight frost will give it a severe attack of cramp. (Edmond Heller, the American zoologist, claimed that a sure cure for this ailment was a bucket of gin, water, and ginger with a kick to it that only an elephant could appreciate. After a couple of such treatments the crafty old patient will feign a return of the malady to get another dose of medicine. In fact, if indulged, the great creature will soon become a regular addict to alcohol.)

Like the typical mammal, the elephant possesses hair, though this statement is rather academic—the short, stiff, sparsely distributed bristles can be better felt than seen. As for the elephant's superbly thick and bushy eyelashes, they are over five inches long, a detail most of us are apt to overlook. The long, ropelike tail has a wiry tuft at the tip. Indian craftsmen wrap the tail hairs with narrow bands of gold and fashion them into bracelets and rings.

The head is massive, the eyes small, the ears large and fanlike. The heavily muscled neck is short, which rather limits the elephant's ability to turn its head. The brain is small in proportion to the size of the body.

The elephant's teeth include the notable second pair of upper incisors that develop into picturesque ivory tusks and continue to grow throughout the life of the animal. We find these tusks foreshadowed in the ancestor of all the elephants—an animal that lived in North Africa during the late Eocene period, about forty-five million years ago.

In this prehistoric creature the rudimentary upper tusks were quite prominent and were directed sharply downward, while the tusks in the lower jaw extended nearly straight ahead and were directed slightly upwards.

In the elephant of today, the molar teeth (the only kind it has, apart from the tusks) are huge blocks, coming into place one at a time on each side of the upper and lower jaws. At no time does an elephant have more than twelve teeth in use. As a tooth wears out, it is gradually pushed forward and falls out, and another moves in from the back to take its place. In its lifetime the animal has twenty-four teeth in all; the first twelve are the milk teeth.

THE FANTASTIC TRUNK

Much of the sense of wonderment we feel when we see an elephant is due to its amazing trunk. This proboscis, as the scientists call it, impresses not only little children but savants as well. (We can gather as much from the scientific name of the elephant order, which is Proboscidea.) The long, flexible, and muscular trunk is really the elephant's lengthened nose and upper lip. (The name "trunk", by the way, appears to be based on a misunderstanding, the word having been confused with the French *trompe*, which means "trumpet" or "proboscis". But, whether the term was originally right or wrong, we all know what is meant by the elephant's trunk.)

Obviously, the elephant did not develop this formidable appendage overnight. The fossil record shows us that as the prehistoric elephants became bulkier and bulkier and taller and taller, the neck shortened and the head and enormous tusks grew in size. Obtaining food would have become an arduous process if the massive creature had not developed a prehensile (grasping) upper lip which gradually evolved into a trunk for gathering things to eat.

And the elephant, a strict vegetarian, has quite a bit of food to gather! It must feed almost constantly to support its enormous body; its daily requirements are about a quarter of a ton of green fodder—or about 150 pounds of hay—and fifty gallons of water. The elephant's menu consists of foliage, grass canes, fruit, tubers, and bark; its favourite delicacy is the tender twigs and branches from the upper limbs of trees.

The giraffe, as you know, has a spectacular way of getting at high branches; the elephant's method of getting at the topmost branches is quite different. It simply pushes the tree over—not with its trunk, but with the front of its head and the great tusks. Getting behind the tree, the pachyderm rocks it with one, two, three steady surges; then a final mighty heave, and down it comes. Such a tree may have a trunk two to four feet around.

Thick and well protected on the outside, the elephant's trunk is delicate and sensitive inside; the animal is careful to guard it from heavy, smashing blows. The margin of the free end is formed into a lobe or lobes used as fingers to pick up small objects. In feeding, the trunk serves as an arm and hand for grasping the food, which is then brought to the mouth to be chewed and swallowed.

The elephant does not, as many suppose, drink through the trunk. Instead, it sucks up water and squirts it into the mouth. The proboscis also serves as a spray gun when the animal bathes itself in either water or dust—both of which it habitually enjoys.

The elephant has poor eyesight and its hearing is only fair; hence its sense of smell is very important. It is probably the most acute sense of smell in the animal kingdom, and it is located in the trunk. Watch the great creature, and you will observe that the trunk is constantly in motion, twisting and uncurling to catch the slightest taint of human or other contamination in the breeze.

Its wonderful trunk serves the elephant in many other ways. Not only is it used to test the wind—the animal examines suspicious objects and dangerous ground with it as well. The appendage is employed in lifting, and can hoist a weight of almost a ton; it has, on occasion, hurled a man a good forty yards.

The elephant even uses its trunk to express affection. During courtship, a cow elephant and a bull elephant caress each other with their trunks, and the cow is ever fondling her calf with her trunk.

In this multi-purpose organ, it has been said, there are 40,000-odd muscles. But whether there are more or fewer need concern us little —the trunk is a superb tool for elephant endeavours, and helps to make its possessor one of the wonders of the animal world.

AMENITIES OF ELEPHANT LIFE

The elephant is a herd animal. A big bull is the nominal leader, but in the field a wise old cow usually takes the lead. When on the march, the band travels in single file. Going down steep slopes, elephants slide on their bellies, with the back legs stretched out behind and the front legs extended forward.

As among all herd animals, the mature males are fierce rivals for supremacy. An old leader beaten in battle is not tolerated by his conqueror and is driven away. His wounded pride makes him irritable and bad-tempered. Such a solitary male usually turns "rogue"—a sulky, dangerous individual, looking for trouble and tearing trees out of the ground just to work off his tantrum.

There is no fixed mating season among elephants. From time to time the males carry on in an irresponsible and frenzied manner. This behaviour, which apparently coincides with breeding intervals, is known as "must" or "musth". At such times the animals are cross-grained, moody, and generally unreliable.

Twenty-one months or so after mating time, a single calf is born covered with coarse black hair. It stands about three feet at the shoulder and weighs approximately two hundred pounds. The calf sheds its milk tusks five or six months after birth, but it continues to suckle for another two years and remains under its mother's care for two years longer.

An elephant is ready to mate at eleven or twelve years; it reaches maturity at fourteen, or thereabouts, though it continues to increase in size and weight for some time after. What we might call the "wisdom tooth", the last tooth to make its appearance, is pushed into place when the animal is some forty years old. The life expectancy of elephants is somewhat less than is popularly supposed; the usual range probably is not more than fifty to sixty years. The maximum recorded life span of eighty-four lacks definite confirmation.

ELEPHANTS ON SHOW

Today no zoo is complete without an elephant, but in former times seeing one of these giants was a rare and memorable occasion. The first captive Asiatic elephant to arrive in America was a two-year-old female brought from Calcutta to New York in 1796. The first African elephant to reach American shores arrived in New York in 1815 on a clipper ship from Liverpool.

The most famous of all elephants, or at least the one that received the most publicity, was Jumbo, purchased by P. T. Barnum from the London Zoological Society in 1882 for ten thousand dollars. The announcement of the sale filled all England with indignation; parents wrote agitated letters to the Press, little children begged Barnum to spare their pet. John Ruskin, the Prince of Wales, and even Queen Victoria implored the Zoological Society to go back on its word. The House of Commons debated Jumbo's status, *The Times* devoted a leading article and an editorial to Jumbo, and a suit was brought in the Court of Chancery to block the elephant's departure.

But Barnum was inexorable, and Jumbo arrived in New York on the *Assyrian Monarch*. The animal's transportation is said to have cost the famous showman an additional twenty thousand dollars. However, he recouped his costs handsomely, as Jumbo was a great favourite from the start. Jumbo, who is reported to have come originally from south of Lake Chad in the French Sudan, did not last long amid the perils of the New World: he was killed by a train in the freight yards at St. Thomas, Ontario, in 1885, at the age of twenty-four. The elephant's skeleton is on exhibition at the American Museum of Natural History in New York; the mounted skin is at Tufts College in Massachusetts. Jumbo stood ten feet nine inches at the shoulder and weighed six tons at the time of his death. His name, perhaps, will prove to be the most durable part of him; today it is applied to peanuts, sandwiches, photographs, and a host of other objects, having become a synonym for large size.

There is something about elephants that seems almost human. For the most part, they are friendly and kindly creatures. They have proved willing assistants to man and are credited with reasoning ability that ranks with that of the dog, the horse, and some of the great apes.

The elephant's first reaction to man is to hate him and distrust him more than any other creature on earth. Yet, once tamed, an elephant not only has complete confidence in its trainer—it is gentle, affectionate, and most considerate to children. Jumbo, when he travelled by rail, always had his keeper in a compartment of his car. A little door was cut in the partition so that during the night Jumbo could reach through with his trunk, touch his keeper, and thus be reassured that his friend and companion was there with him.

There is no doubt that Jumbo loved children. He never failed to make sympathetic response to the timid gestures of the youngsters when they presented their little offerings. His greatest joy seemed to be in giving a load of hilarious children a ride on his back; he would kneel on his forelegs, coaxing the fearful tots to climb on to his massive shoulders.

The belief that an elephant will bear a lasting grudge against any individual who has harmed it is far from true. In training, practically all elephants are punished by their trainers—often severely—for mis-behaviour. However, as long as the trainer is sure of himself and commands the respect of the animal, they will be on the best of terms afterwards.

History tells us that the Romans were great showmen and probably the first to exhibit elephants in a circus. According to Pliny, the Circus Maximus in Rome held 260,000 people; such ancient crowds must have thrilled to the spectacle of elephants in action just as we do today.

The American circus, or "rolling show", as it was called, started in 1796 with the arrival of the Asiatic elephant we have mentioned previously. The second elephant to reach America formed the nucleus of what was in time to become the famous Barnum and Bailey circus.

Circus elephants are always females, as bull elephants are apt to become uncontrollable and dangerous at certain seasons of the year. The great animals are one of the main attractions of the circus and zoo. They not only carry children on their backs—they can be taught many interesting tricks, such as playing ball, lying down, standing up on their hind legs, and even standing on their heads.

Apart from their value as entertainers, elephants have been useful

Freelance Photographers Guild

FAVOURITE PASTIME

While they are very particular about the water they drink, elephants will bathe anywhere the opportunity presents itself. The trunk, which is really the outsized nose and upper lip, is said to have 40,000 muscles, and it serves the elephant in many ways. If the very short neck limits the ability of the huge beast to turn its head, the constantly twitching, weaving trunk picks up the faintest scent from any direction; and its spray-gun action makes a wonderful shower bath—for the elephant! *See page 623.*

Freelance Photographers Guild

LIVING FOSSILS

Fossilized tapir remains indicate that there has been little or no change in these animals for 20 million years and that present-day species differ only slightly from those in existence 40 million years ago. Surviving only in the jungle areas of Central and South America and the Malay Peninsula, the two widely separated groups differ mainly in the colour patterns of the adults—the Malay tapir a sharp contrast of black head, neck and legs with a white body, and the New World varieties a more uniform black or dark brown. All young tapirs have the distinctive white or fawn coloured stripes on a dark background. *See page 667.*

[6-1]

Largest of land animals, the elephant uniquely combines tremendous size and graceful, rhythmic motion, the ultimate of brute strength and careful reason, the whole tempered with a crafty, puckish sense of humour.

See page 628

[6-1A]

From the so-obvious trunk to the seldom noticed luxuriant eyelashes—wild or tame, the true "king" of beasts is a never-ending source of wonder.

See page 628

[6-2]

While many of the once numerous variants of the African wild donkey tribe are now extinct in the wild state, the Somali wild ass still exists in limited numbers. Closely related to the horse, it is believed to be the stock from which our domesticated donkeys were derived.   *See page 661*

The zebra is another African representative of the horse family. Its pattern is correctly described as dark or black stripes on a nearly white background, rather than white stripes on a dark animal. Zebras resist being put to work and are more stubborn than donkeys.
See page 662

[6-2A]

to man in India for logging operations and hunting expeditions. In Africa the ivory trade has flourished for centuries. For about a thousand years the elephant played a role in ancient warfare.

THE ELEPHANT GOES TO WAR

Given the enormous size and strength of the elephant, we must rank it as one of man's great triumphs that he was able to tame and exploit this massive giant. The Carthaginians, those great traders and colonizers of old, domesticated elephants; the ancient people of India trained elephants from time immemorial and, as you will see later on, put them to excellent use in logging operations.

In the early days of Asiatic civilization the elephant played an important role in warfare. It was used chiefly in battering down fortified defences—many of the gates of Indian cities were covered with long iron spikes as a protective measure to stop elephants forcing open the city's barriers. When chess was invented in India, about A.D. 600 or thereabouts, one of the pieces was an elephant. Since chess is essentially a war game, at least as far as its origin is concerned, we can conclude that the military use of elephants must have been quite common in India.

The Indians used elephants in an effort to stem the advance of the army of Alexander the Great—this was about 320 B.C. The animals served much as tanks do today—the Indians mounted several archers in each howdah, with a view to supporting the infantry with added firepower. But the Macedonian foot and horse were well disciplined and apparently held their ground against this strange enemy.

The battle of Heraclea, fought in 280 B.C. by the forces of King Pyrrhus against the Romans, seems to have been the first time elephants were put into action against the Romans. Pyrrhus used his elephants as heavy cavalry, sending them in massed charges to trample down the Roman infantry. The effect was apparently quite terrifying, and the Romans were routed. However, Pyrrhus lost so many men that his victory was worthless—hence the phrase "Pyrrhic victory".

This was not the end of the elephants' career as fighters. The most famous instance of the military use of the beasts was in Hannibal's great victory over the Romans at Cannae, one of the decisive battles of world history, fought in 218 B.C. It must have required no little ingenuity on Hannibal's part to transport his thirty-seven elephants across the Alps (he invaded Italy not by sea, as we might have expected, but through Spain and southern France).

We do not know whether Hannibal used African or Asiatic elephants, nor have we full details about just how he employed them against the Romans. But there seems little doubt that they must have had a very intimidating effect on the Romans, who were beholding the great, strange-looking creatures at their gates for the first time.

About six hundred years ago, when Tamerlane defeated Prince Mohammed at Delhi, he captured three thousand elephants, some of which he used in building the great mosque at Samarkand.

Though the Chinese domesticated horses and cattle at an early date, they made no mention of domesticated elephants until the Six Dynasties (A.D. 386-589).

AFRICAN ELEPHANTS

The Bush Elephant, *Loxodonta africana*, is the largest of present-day elephants. It reaches a maximum shoulder height of thirteen feet and weighs over six tons. However, bulls rarely exceed eleven feet, and cows are about seven feet at the shoulder. You can distinguish the bush elephant of Africa from the Asiatic species by the more blackish skin colour, the larger ears, and more rounded, sloping forehead. Another difference is that in the African type the back is highest at the shoulder; the Asiatic elephant's back is slightly hollowed out at the shoulder. These two forms are all that is left of the family Elephantidae today.

The favourite fastness of the African elephant is the dense, shadeless bush, little taller than itself, but it also haunts the mountain forests, the giant grass veldt, the bamboo forests and the reed swamps. Despite its enormous size and ponderous build, an African elephant can move through the bush as silently as almost any other animal.

On one occasion, when stalking an enormous bull, the author and his party suddenly saw its great form, covered with red dust, wavering above him, less than twenty-five yards away. Its trunk was extended straight out, waving gently to catch his scent. As he stood spellbound at the apparition, it vanished in the thick bush so silently and quickly that he almost doubted what he had actually seen.

Backtracking the animal's trail, the writer found tracks that showed the elephant had circled to see who the intruders were and had stood within ten feet of them, watching them go by. From its point of vantage it could have killed the whole party with little effort, if it had so desired.

The enormous ears of the African elephant serve as fans, and are kept constantly in motion during the heat of the day to circulate the air. Each ear is about three and one-half feet wide—over four feet wide and five feet long in large bulls. In these, the spread across the extended ears, including the head, is fully ten feet.

GIANT AMONG THE MAMMALS

The male bush elephant of Africa may stand a dozen feet in height, and weigh over six tons. His huge ears, each about three and one-half feet wide, serve as fans, keeping the air around the animal moving. A full-grown African elephant seldom lies down to sleep. For the last thirty or forty years of his life, he slumbers in a standing position.

The trunk, which may measure up to ninety-eight inches for a large bull, has two finger-like extensions at the tip. There are three toes on the hind feet and five on the forefeet, but all we can see of the toes is the broad nails. The tail may be as much as fifty-seven inches long, with a fifteen-inch tuft of bristles at the tip.

Both bulls and cows have tusks. In the female they are usually smaller and more slender, but some cow-elephant tusks have reached almost six feet in length. The greatest tusk on record weighed 226 pounds and was over ten feet long.

ELEPHANTS WITH FOUR TUSKS

Years ago the natives in the remotest forests of the then Belgian Congo used to tell stories about elephants with two sets of tusks. A few open-minded scholars believed that there might be such creatures— survivors, perhaps, of the now extinct mastodons. A search revealed no such animal, and these tales were forgotten, filed away as native folklore.

But four-tusked elephants are not a myth. Every twenty years or so, one is either shot or found dead. There is a splendid example of an elephant skull with four tusks in the Congo Museum in Belgium and another in the Explorers Club in New York. Most, if not all such skulls have come from the Congo. However, apart from the extra pair of perfectly formed tusks, the creatures are no different from other elephants that live in the same region; we can attribute their peculiarity to nothing more exciting than accidental variation.

ELEPHANTS AT REST AND IN MOTION

From about the time an African elephant reaches maturity until the moment it dies, it never lies down. Amazing as it may seem, the African elephant generally sleeps standing up for the last thirty or forty years of its life! It appears to be able to enjoy enough repose while in a standing position. The fact that its legs are built like supporting columns may explain why this stance is restful for the beast.

Young elephants, and occasionally some full-grown ones, sleep stretched out on their side. With a calf elephant it is an easy matter to lie down; but as it grows older and heavier, the task of lowering its huge bulk to the ground and raising it again when the elephant gets up, becomes increasingly difficult. In going down, the animal bends the front legs forward at the elbows and the hind legs backward at the knees. The elephant then rolls over on its side and stretches out. (The elephant's height, by the way, is approximately twice the circumference of the forefoot; often this measurement turns out to be remarkably accurate.)

Ordinarily an elephant walks at a fast shuffle; a rate of six to eight miles per hour is common. When enraged, this ponderous beast can charge for fifty yards at a speed of twenty-five miles per hour. Normally it cannot jump even a narrow ditch—its huge body must have support fore and aft at all times. However, a charging bull has been known to clear a wide ditch, though it was lame for some time afterwards.

Elephants know—and follow—the best routes through the forests and mountains. Many of the highways in Africa today proceed along the routes originally laid out by elephants. They can climb steep embankments and slide down them or walk along a narrow ledge three feet wide. In some instances, they grasp roots or branches to lever themselves up and over rocks.

When undisturbed, elephants make a peculiar rumbling sound which is apparently due to the workings of the digestive system—at least that is what it sounds like to the author. These rumblings can be heard a quarter of a mile away. When disturbed, the elephant stills the sound so as not to betray its presence.

African elephants are fond of bathing, but they are fastidious about the kind of water they drink. In Kenya the author found that they came a long way to dig holes in the sand of a dry river bed to get clean water, ignoring a fast-flowing river with chocolate-coloured water. The water pit is not dug with the tusks; about two feet deep, it is sunk by scraping with the forefeet and sending the sand and gravel flying.

The African elephant is generally conceded to be less tractable than its Indian cousin, though just as intelligent. Despite its more independent character, the African variety can be domesticated and trained for clearing land and other laborious farm work. The bush elephant was once common over most of the continent and frequented all types of country from plains and jungles to mountains ten thousand feet high. It is still holding its own in some parts of Equatorial Africa, where three subspecies are known to exist.

The Forest Elephant, *Loxodonta cyclotis*, makes its home in the rain forests of West Africa from Sierra Leone to Angola and east to the basin of the Congo River. On a comparative basis we can call it "little", as it rarely exceeds eight feet at the shoulder. Its ears, too, are relatively small and rounded for an African species. As for the hind feet, they usually have four toes instead of three. Immature forest elephants have been mistaken for pygmy elephants, but, given time, they always grow up unless artificially stunted.

AFRICAN ELEPHANT GRAVEYARDS—REAL OR IMAGINARY?

The legend of elephant graveyards—places where numbers of elephants go to die—is still believed by many African natives. They claim there is only one graveyard and that all elephants go there to meet their end. Nothing is ever said about rhino, giraffe, or antelope graveyards. What gives the legend a certain plausibility is the fact that the bones of a single elephant are rarely found.

In the early part of the eighteenth century, the Portuguese often came upon great piles of elephant tusks in Angola, but no skeletons. Sometimes the heaps, containing four tons of ivory, were surmounted by carved wooden idols and human skulls. At this distance in time, we can only guess at the meaning of such finds. Probably the natives had gathered the tusks. The skeletons may have been lost and scattered over a wide area.

After a bush fire in the late 1930's, an elephant-control officer discovered an area where there was a large collection of both elephant skeletons and ivory. It was supposed they were from wounded elephants that had gone there to die. At least the natives claimed they had seen many of the beasts go there—often they wounded them, but were afraid to follow and collect the ivory.

Vernon Brelsford, writing in the *African Wild Life Journal*, tells of the island of Minswa in the swamps of northern Rhodesia, a favourite retreat for elephants. One or two natives, he says, have gone to the island but never returned; no white man has ventured there. Brelsford himself canoed round its edges and heard the screams of elephants but refrained from landing. He believes there is a graveyard there —but says it is also a nursery and a home for very-much-alive elephants.

Time and again, large piles of elephant bones have been found in one place or another; but it is assumed that these represent herds massacred by natives or white men, for there are usually skeletons but no tusks. All in all, then, the great elephant cemetery, as such, appears to be a myth.

ELEPHANTS STICK TOGETHER

Most of us have heard rumours that elephants will not desert a comrade in distress and will even help it to escape if it has been wounded. One of the foremost authorities on African big game produced unquestionable proof that such rumours have a genuine basis in fact.

When Carl Akeley shot a big bull elephant, the great creature dropped, fatally wounded. Shortly afterwards, coming up over a rise, Akeley saw two other elephants, one on either side of the wounded animal, lifting it to its feet and trying their utmost to guide its faltering steps to safety. Ten or twelve other elephants gave assistance with their tusks and trunks in an effort to get their stricken relative back on his feet.

So impressed was he with this display of chivalry that Akeley executed the scene as he saw it, in bronze, for the American Museum of Natural History, as a lasting tribute to these great creatures of the African veldt.

Akeley tells us some other curious things about these animals. Not the least interesting is the fact that baby elephants have playthings. He describes a sunbaked mud ball, two and a half feet in diameter, with which he saw a group of young elephants playing. They rolled it half a mile or more.

ASIATIC ELEPHANTS

The Asiatic or Indian Elephant, *Elephas maximus*, dwells in India, Ceylon, Burma, Indo-China, and the Malay Peninsula. After the cow the elephant is the second most venerated beast of the Hindus; the Hindu god Ganesh had the head of an elephant. The Buddhists class the elephant with the dove of peace. One of their legends tells of an elephant in "musth" that was sent to kill the Lord Buddha. They met, but when Buddha touched the beast on the forehead, it bowed low before him.

HOW ELEPHANTS ARE CAPTURED

There are several methods used in capturing elephants. Large, highly prized bulls are tracked down and taken in a simple but ingenious manner. Mahouts (professional elephant drivers), mounted on tame females, single out the desired bull. They then make their mounts available to him. In the course of becoming successively acquainted with the entire relay of females, the bull is kept awake day and night and finally succumbs to exhaustion and sleep. The bull wakes to find himself securely chained.

The method for capturing elephant herds is to drive them into an enclosure. While one group of men build the enclosure, or *kheddah*, another group surround the area about the herd by hastily constructing a bamboo fence. The *kheddah* itself is a corral formed of stout twelve-foot timbers set in a circle twenty to fifty feet in diameter. with a four-yard gap through which the herd is driven by native beaters.

In Nepal and Bengal, elephants are sometimes noosed or lassoed. Two tame elephants approach the wild one from either side, and the mahout throws the noose around its neck. In Ceylon, hand-roping is customary; but in Mysore, they capture elephants by driving them into pitfalls about ten feet long, seven and one-half feet wide, and fifteen feet deep. It is a tight fit, but the beast does not injure itself trying to escape.

HOW THE INDIAN ELEPHANT SLEEPS

The Asiatic elephant, unlike its African cousin, lies down to rest. When it is ready to go to sleep, it stands motionless in the forest like a statue. After about an hour, when the world is fast asleep, the elephant goes down so suddenly and quietly that in a flash of the eyelids its dark shadow seems to vanish in the air. It usually sleeps in two "shifts" —one from about ten in the morning to three in the afternoon, and the other from eleven at night to three in the morning.

COURTSHIP AND BRINGING UP THE YOUNG

Elephants do not readily breed in captivity, though captive animals will breed normally in natural surroundings. As elephants are shy about their love affairs, they have a hankering for privacy. One fantastic story tells how a female preparing for a honeymoon digs a pit, stocking around it several weeks' supply of fruits and fodder for herself and the prospective bridegroom. Here she waits, trumpeting love calls to her mate.

Normally a male and female elephant go through several days and even weeks of courtship. Then, for a month more the pair will graze and live together. Once the honeymoon is over, a female seeks the close friendship of another female and they remain inseparable until some time after the calf is born. It takes the watchful care of both to protect the calf from tigers. Most females first mate between the ages of eighteen and twenty-one.

In the natural state, most elephant calves are born in the spring, between March and April. The coming into the world of a baby elephant is quite an event in a herd of wild elephants. Calves are usually born during the night. There is a constant bellowing and trumpeting among the elders to herald the occasion. This terrifying din doubtless serves the purpose of scaring away marauders—especially tigers. For the first few weeks after the arrival of a calf, a herd will stay put in one locality and more or less keep a closed circle around the mother and her calf, particularly at night.

During the early days of the baby's life the mother, if disturbed, will pick up her calf with her trunk and carry it away to safety.

A baby elephant follows at its mother's heels for at least three or four years and is suckled at the breasts between her forelegs. On one occasion a sacred white elephant calf at the Mandalay palace whose mother died was reared by twenty-five Burmese women who suckled it.

Up to the age of five, the elephant's trunk is of little use to it; but at this time the youngster begins to gather fodder and gradually ceases to depend on its mother's milk. Females average four or five calves during a lifetime. Twins are occasionally born, and it is not uncommon for two calves of different ages to be following one mother. Occasionally a female will have as many as eight calves in a lifetime; one female reportedly gave birth to a calf on her sixty-first birthday.

At sixteen, young elephants have reached the adolescent stage and males begin flirting with females; but the bulls exhibit no sign of "musth" until they are over twenty-one. Musth is shown by a discharge of a strong-smelling waxy substance or fluid from glands near the eyes, just above the mouth. It normally occurs during hot weather and may last two weeks. From the age of thirty-five to forty-five the discharge is greatest and marks the period in which an elephant is in its prime; musth is usually connected with sexual excitement.

During musth the bull goes on a rampage and cannot be trusted. Often the fluid drips down on to his mouth, which makes him even more ferocious. At the age of fifty, the discharge of fluid from the musth glands has subsided and finally disappears.

Animals in musth are not to be confused with rogue elephants that plunder and destroy. It is the social outcast that in some way has broken the laws of the herd and been expelled that becomes a savage, brooding rogue. Rogues that have been wounded and caused to suffer by man may also become a menace to all and everything they encounter. In ancient days a rogue elephant filled the office of public executioner in India. Occasionally there are female rogues.

ELEPHANTS AT WORK

It is curious that an elephant in the wild state, so suspicious and distrustful of man, should become one of the gentlest, most dependable, and most trustworthy of animals when domesticated.

Elephants have greater learning capacity than most animals; in fact, trained elephants never stop learning. They understand about twenty-five words of command.

When a trained elephant passes an implement, such as a spear, to a rider on its back, it soon learns to pass the handle and not the point. When going through a forest, an elephant is always careful to guard against the chance that its rider or riders may get struck by twigs or branches. It will pull away the small obstructing twigs with its trunk, push over small trees and go around the low, heavy branches of large trees.

Occasionally elephants try to play innocent tricks on their riders and squeal with delight when successful. Young elephants form a naughty habit of using clay to plug the bells worn around the neck so that they can steal bananas from cultivated plantations at night without being detected. Like children, they feel that stolen fruit is the sweetest.

A great deal has been written about the intelligence of the elephant. There seem to be grounds for believing that it has more reasoning power than either a dog or a horse. Here is a most interesting example of elephant reasoning:

In Burma, one of these beasts was ordered to lift a large log to an elevated position. When the animal realized that its burden might roll over its head and crush the rider, it suddenly dropped the log— and then did the job in its own way. This time, without any instructions from the mahout, the animal seized a clublike piece of the wood and jammed it in between its trunk and tusks in a vertical position. Balancing the log on its tusks, the elephant raised it without any danger of its falling back on the rider; finally the beast placed its forefeet on a log to gain elevation and set the timber in place.

THE SACRED ELEPHANT

The Asiatic or Indian elephant, sacred to adherents of the Hindu religion, is smaller in size than its relatives in Africa. This animal is also easily recognized by its less conspicuous ears. Famed as a worker, the Indian elephant aids the Asiatic natives in moving timber.

TAMING AND TRAINING THE ELEPHANT

It has been calculated that it costs about five thousand dollars to rear an elephant to the age when it begins to earn its own living. Used for farm purposes and for carrying great loads, the Asiatic elephant is easy to domesticate even if captured when adult. Its strength and intelligence are especially valuable in the teak forests, where the elephant shows remarkable ability, as we have just seen, to handle big timber. Bulls are most useful for this purpose, since their tusks are larger. An elephant can carry up to one ton (an average load is six hundred pounds), and can drag a two-ton log. It is claimed that during the

Second World War the Japanese loaded their elephants to the extent of four tons per animal.

Wild elephants are usually taken at the age of eighteen or nineteen —the age at which they can start doing light work. However, these are rarely quite as serviceable as ranch-raised animals, for the cuts and burns from the ropes lashed around the feet of trapped elephants never heal completely.

Baby elephants go to school soon after they are weaned. A wise old female takes charge of perhaps half a dozen or more. An elephant is trained in about the same way as a horse, but the process is much slower. The calf is corralled in a small pen with a leather thong around one foot for control. A native boy, or *oozie* as he is called in Burma, is lowered on to its head by a pulley and raised when the calf bucks. This is kept up until the young elephant grows tired and gets used to the operation. By that time it will permit the *oozie* to sit quietly on its head.

Usually the mother elephant is permitted to stand by; her presence helps quiet her child, and she raises no objection to what is going on. The youngster learns its first lesson in less than twelve hours, and good behaviour is rewarded with choice fruit. The next day the trainers repeat the lesson in the open, placing a light load on the pupil's back. Once this ordeal has been passed, the candidate is sent to school with other young elephants, where it is taught obedience and proper behaviour.

This goes on for another ten years. By the time each growing individual has reached the age of fourteen years, it has been assigned a rider about its own age. Usually the two become inseparable and go through life together until death takes one of them. There is no one so proud as the copper-skinned Indian boy riding on his elephant. He knows every whim and fault of his companion. He scrubs the elephant from the tip of the trunk to the end of the tail with soap and water every morning, and then polishes the tusks with sand until they are gleaming white.

Though the elephant is ready for light work at the age of nineteen or so, it is not given really difficult tasks until it is twenty-five or older. By "light work" we mean going out with the experienced elephants to the mountains and helping move the heavy teak logs down impassable slopes to the rivers below.

Working elephants have a hard life—they must labour all day and then forage for their own food during the evening and night. The ones that are well cared for, work three days at a time and then rest the next two days. This goes on for nine months, after which the animals are given a complete rest for three months.

Elephants dislike nervous people and they refuse to be hurried. An elephant will be out of sorts all day if it is suddenly wakened in the morning. It likes to dawdle while it thinks about getting up. The elephant boy or mahout is well aware of this trait; after finding his elephant in the morning, he sits down close by and speaks gently to the great animal until such time as it condescends to arouse itself.

Elephants are still used as saddle animals, though much less so than formerly. They appear in religious rituals, processions, and other ceremonial events; occasionally they are still employed in hunting big game. A full-dress equipage, including the howdah, gold saddle-cloth, punkahs, ropes and other gear, adds up to about half a ton.

ASIATIC ELEPHANTS ARE "SMALLER"

Though Asiatic elephants are smaller than the African variety, they are anything but small.

The Asiatic elephant reaches a shoulder height of about nine feet —very large bulls may stand ten feet. The average weight of an Asiatic elephant is approximately three and one-half tons, with a maximum of six tons. The skin is grey, lighter in tone and somewhat smoother in texture than the hide of the African varieties.

Once in a while we come across a "white" Asiatic elephant—not really snow-white but rather clouded by a slate-grey cast. The experts distinguish three subspecies of Asiatic elephants, although for the most part the differences are not too clearly marked. There is one clear-cut distinction in the case of the Sumatra elephant—it has no tusks.

The Asiatic elephant has a bulging, protuberant forehead, but its ears are relatively small as compared with those of the African elephant. The tusks of the male reach a length of about eight feet—ten at most. The greatest recorded weight for one tusk is 126 pounds. In the female, tusks are either lacking or else so reduced in size that they rarely project beyond the lips. The trunk has only one finger-like lobe at the margin of the tip. There are five toes on the front feet and four toes on the hind feet.

ELEPHANT GRAVEYARDS IN ASIA

According to legend there are elephant graveyards in Asia as well as in Africa. Tradition has it that as its time draws near, the gaunt, aged Asiatic elephant makes its last long pilgrimage to these isolated spots to wait for death. Here, so we are told, the ground is strewn with huge bones bleached white in the tropical sun, and with ivory tusks that signify fabulous wealth for the finder.

While there are no elephant graveyards in the popular sense, the legend is not entirely groundless. Elephants do have a place where they go to die. Worn-out patriarchs that are reaching the end of their days seek the shade of the upper river valleys where food is plentiful and easy to get.

The end usually comes toward the close of the hot dry season. For a last drink, the weary old elephants, their cheeks now sunken, climb down into the almost dry river beds and here spray their hot, feverish bodies with water and cool sand. There they stay until, growing dizzy, they stagger and fall. At last the great old heart stops and all is still.

The vultures and hyenas take over; then come the monsoons— torrents of water carrying thousands of tons of mud and soil rush down the valley and bury all that is left of the once great creatures in tombs that are hidden for all time. Such is the end of an old elephant, but there is no long, weary trek to a common graveyard to die.

Hyraxes or Old World Conies—
Little Cousins of the Elephant

PICTURE, if you can, a rabbit without a tail, and with short legs and small ears. This will give you some idea of what a hyrax looks like. Hyraxes, also known as "dassies" or "conies", are rock-dwellers for the most part, though a few dwell in trees. Excellent climbers, they can scale the face of an almost perpendicular rock or tree trunk. They are very active, timid little creatures, always on the alert, ready to dive for safety in the rocks on the least provocation.

Limited to the Old World, the hyraxes are spread over most of Africa, and have a range that extends north through the Arab countries to Asia. They have found their way into the folklore of these regions. Thus, to the Zulu the alarm call of the hyrax is *Ma-'ng afa*, meaning "I am dying". In Natal, the natives claim that the hyrax is the only mammal that can stare directly at the sun.

These strange little animals have such marked peculiarities that scientists have placed them in an order all by themselves (Hyracoidea). Hyraxes are vegetarians, and their teeth are of the kind we see in certain hoofed mammals, particularly rhinoceroses. From their foot structure, we can tell that somewhere along the line in past history there was probably a connection between these little fellows and the lordly elephants. The four-toed feet of hyraxes end in blunt claws resembling miniature hoofs. As for the soles of the feet, they are naked, but cushioned with well-developed foot pads.

The family Procaviidae, which takes in all the hyraxes, is divided into three groups. The species making up these groups are all very similar in size, appearance, and general structure.

The Grey Hyrax, or Rock Hyrax, *Heterohyrax*, lives among rocks in colonies ranging from half a dozen to fifty animals. They feed on green vegetation during daylight hours but may continue feeding into the night. The young—there are two or three in a litter—are fully clothed and have their eyes open at birth.

These sociable creatures have a shrill communicating cry. When a hyrax looks outside its den and finds no imminent danger, it gives the all-clear signal. This is relayed by other members of the colony until the rocks resound with their cheerful voices.

——HYRAX OF THE BIBLE. There are several passages in the Bible where the word *shaphan* occurs. Translators have rendered this word as "cony", under the impression that a rabbit was meant. However, the reference is most likely to the Syrian Hyrax or Daman, *Heterohyrax syriacus*, which dwells in Syria and Palestine.

In the Old Testament we find such passages as, "and the cony, because he cheweth the cud and divideth not the hoof . . ." and "the high hills are a refuge for the wild goats, and the rocks for the conies". These descriptions enable us to recognize the hyrax—although the animal does not actually chew the cud. However, the hyrax does live in holes in the rocks and is extremely wary and timid, bearing out Solomon's remarks about its habits.

The Tree Hyrax, *Dendrohyrax,* has longer and softer fur than the rock hyrax and is a little larger in size. A native of the heavily forested regions of Central and South Africa, especially of the Congo, the tree hyrax is a solitary creature. Usually a single animal makes its home in a hollow trunk or in the thick foliage of a tree. Frequenting only the tallest of forest trees, it feeds on the leaves of the uppermost branches. It restricts its wanderings to the night, never leaving its roost until after sunset.

ITS FAMILY TREE CONTAINS AN ELEPHANT

The unprepossessing little hyrax, a creature that looks like a rabbit, is in an order of mammals all by itself. This is so because it has certain features not found collectively in any other animal. Interestingly enough, its feet reveal a relationship to the elephant. The hyrax is fond of sitting among rocks and sunning itself, and is noted for the noise it makes. It is much preyed upon by wild dogs. Shown here is the rock hyrax.

However, you must not conclude that the tree hyrax lives an exclusively "lone-wolf" existence, for it carries on a continual discourse with its neighbours. Its cry is a long-drawn-out howl or roar, swelling in volume. This goes on for half an hour, almost without interruption. It is only the males that howl, usually one at a time. These performances may last from soon after sundown until two o'clock in the morning.

Families are not large; occasionally there are twins, rarely more. The young—as among the rock hyraxes—are born fully furred and with eyes wide open.

[6-3]

The South American tapir is one of several species of Tapiridae which inhabit Central America and the northern part of South America. Scientists classify the tapir and the horse together as "odd-toed" hoofed mammals because they have an enlarged third toe, encased in a hoof, on which they place all or most of their weight when walking or running.   See page 668

The Malay tapir and its New World cousins represent the last of a once wide-spread family. Shy, inoffensive creatures with the ability to stay under water for a remarkably long time, they live a solitary life in marshes and along watercourses.
                                                                    See page 670

[6-3A]

There is no question of domesticating or making a pet of this member of the odd-toed clan. A suspicious, near-sighted, not too bright animal, the huge, ungainly black rhinoceros of East Africa will courteously yield right of way to the elephant —all others beware! *See page 672*

[6-4]

The Big-toothed Hyrax, *Procavia,* the common African type that lives in colonies, is found almost anywhere on the continent where there are sizable outcrops of rock. Its head-and-body length is about twenty inches; the tail is a mere stub, less than an inch long. The rather coarse fur is brownish grey, though the shade varies quite a bit.

The Horse Family and the Tapirs

WHEN SCIENTISTS want to explain how the strange animals of the past—the weird-looking creatures whose bones we see in museums —developed into our familiar modern mammals, they often take the horse as an example. And with good reason—what could be more remarkable and clearer than the development of the "Dawn Horse" (Eohippus), a little, foxlike creature only eleven inches high, into the tall and stately horse that we know so well today?

The origin of the horse dates back some sixty million years to the Eocene period—the "Dawn Age" of mammals. The early horses appeared almost simultaneously in Europe and America. These small creatures had four toes on the front feet and three toes on the hind feet.

It was in America that the horses passed through the greater part of their evolution. Having neither horns nor claws to protect themselves with, they had to depend on speed. In the course of millions of years, the centre toes, which bore most of the animal's weight, grew larger and larger, while the outside toes became smaller and smaller. What was left in the end was one vastly enlarged "toe"— the hoof. This was naturally much more suitable for swift running on hard, dry land than the original toes which it replaced. At the same time, horses grew in size; their weight increased from the hundred pounds or so of the Dawn Horse to the thousand pounds and more of later horses.

The horse seems to have had a chequered career—after all, a lot can happen in sixty million years. We possess good evidence that the horse died out in Europe at an early date; as for Asia, its supply of horses was restocked from America by way of a land bridge that once joined Siberia with Alaska.

However, America cannot claim the honour of having produced the immediate ancestor of our domestic horse. It seems that the entire tribe of American horses vanished during the Ice Age. The modern horse, then, originated in Europe or Asia. It was the Spaniards who reintroduced the animal into America.

THE HORSE IN HISTORY

It is hard for us to realize, in this age of high-powered cars and jet-propelled aircraft, what an important role the horse played in man's history for thousands of years. Horses were known to the Babylonians as far back as 2,300 B.C. and were used by them to draw their war chariots beginning about 1,700 B.C. It was the horse that made possible the far-flung conquests of Alexander the Great. Without the horse, the hordes of Alaric and Attila could hardly have managed to make their way west from central Asia to humble the Roman Empire. Again, the great conquests of Genghis Khan are unthinkable without his half-million horsemen. On foot, they would still have been superb soldiers, but they could never have covered as much territory as they did. The medieval knights and the Crusaders were equally dependent on their horses.

In American history we find the same pattern. The Indian warriors of the Plains, the gallant cavalry fighting of the Civil War, the Pony Express, the stage-coach era, the epic of the cowboy—all these distinctive aspects of the American past were made possible by the horse.

Up to the introduction of the railroad, all postal systems had to rely on the horse. Almost three thousand years ago, Herodotus, "the father of history", commented admiringly on the Persian postal system, which made use of swift horses. The Aztecs, on the other hand, had to use human runners, for they lacked horses before the coming of the white man.

When Cortez landed in Mexico, he had only sixteen horses. They

THE HORSE FAMILY AND THE TAPIRS

were the first ever seen by the Aztecs, and these strange, seemingly towering animals struck the Indians with terror. Some twenty years later, when De Soto crossed the Mississippi in 1541, his men either abandoned or lost some of their horses. Most authorities believe that these animals formed the nucleus of the bands of wild horses later found west of the lower Mississippi.

The descendants of these horses came to be known as "mustangs"— an English pronunciation of the Spanish word *mesteno*, which means "strayed" or "wild".

The cayuse (Indian pony), named after an Indian tribe, was part mustang; usually the animal was inferior, due to carelessness in selecting breeding stock.

Horses are long lived and some mares have been known to breed up to the age of twenty-five. One individual lived to be fifty years old —probably a record.

To horsemen, the word "horse" always means a male—the female is invariably called a mare. A young mare is a filly. A young male is called in Britain a colt; a mature male is a stallion, unless it has been gelded, when it is called a gelding. Mares foal eleven months after mating time.

HORSE FEATS

Careful breeding and training of horses have resulted in some remarkable achievements. Man o' War was credited with a speed of 21 seconds for a quarter-mile—an hourly rate of 43 miles. (Of course, speed decreases as more distance is covered.) Trotting horses take a little under two minutes for a mile. Workhorses are noted for their powers of endurance; a large dray horse dragged sixteen railway trucks, weighing 55 tons, on steel tracks over a distance of 20 miles in six hours. The record jump for a hunter is somewhere between 33 and 37 feet.

"A HORSE OF A DIFFERENT COLOUR"

The homely old phrase about "a horse of a different colour" once had a significance which is probably lost on most of us nowadays. Certain breeds of horses invariably have a characteristic colour. Hence the appearance of off-colours betrays to us the presence of crossbreeding or impurities in the breeding stock. There are several standardized horse colours—black, brown, bay, chestnut, dun, cream, white, grey, roan, piebald, appaloosa, and, most beautiful of all, the palomino.

Domestic horses were probably derived from a now extinct large horse of central Europe, a smaller mountain pony, and the Mongolian wild horse which has lived on into our own time. We now have twenty-five or so distinct breeds.

HORSE BREEDING

Man has been breeding horses for centuries. He has many uses for these animals. Sometimes he needs a large, powerful creature; again, he may require speed. Temperament also matters, just as it does among humans: some kinds of horses must be placid, others mettlesome. The prizewinner at the horse show and the pit pony in the coal mine each have their clearly defined roles.

Horses are either purebred or crossbred. If both its parents are of the same breed, a horse is said to be purebred. A crossbred horse, then, is one with parents of different breeds. Purebreeding will intensify a given quality, possibly at the expense of others; crossbreeding, under favourable conditions, has brought about desirable combinations of good qualities.

People are prone to confuse purebred horses with Thoroughbred horses. The distinction is clear-cut and important. A purebred horse may be of any breed, as long as its parents also belonged to that breed. A Thoroughbred is a *specific* breed of horse. Every Thoroughbred is necessarily a purebred horse; but many purebred horses are not Thoroughbreds.

SOME NOTABLE WORKHORSES

The Shire horse, developed in England, is the largest of all horses. It stands some seventeen hands high (sixty-eight inches) and weights of 2,200-2,400 pounds are common. We owe this breed to Henry VIII, who had all horses of less than fifteen hands destroyed because they were eating too much in proportion to the amount of work they could perform. Thus the Shire horse evolved from the mating of large horses.

Another famous draught horse is the Clydesdale, weighing close to a ton. Both energetic and good looking, it is a favourite workhorse in the American Middle West. The Belgian horse, approximating the Shire horse in size and weight, is thought to be descended from the powerful animals that medieval knights used as chargers.

Percherons, originally bred in France, may weigh over a ton. They are exceptionally sturdy, hard-working animals. In the old days, they were the favoured horses for stage-coach travel. In more recent times, Percherons were used a great deal for hauling delivery wagons and fire engines. The coming of the motor-car has put an end to those activities, but to this day Percherons are probably used more than any other kind of horse in circuses.

Shetland ponies have a long and useful history of working in England's coal mines. Despite their small size, they are famous for their powers of endurance. (A pony, by the way, is a small horse—not necessarily a young one.)

GLAMOROUS BREEDS

When we come to the glamorous breeds, the most famous are perhaps the magnificent steeds of the Arabian deserts. These animals have been bred since about A.D. 800. Celebrated for stamina as well as swiftness, they have powerful lungs, slender legs, and broad hoofs. Hundreds of years of selective breeding have made them exceptionally able to resist heat, hunger, and thirst.

For the last four hundred years or so, Arabian horses have been mated with other breeds, producing handsome creatures with many outstanding qualities. The most notable animal of this type is the Thoroughbred, which started in England toward the end of the seventeenth century, when three Arabian stallions were bred to swift, light English mares. Later, Thoroughbreds were taken to America. The finest Thoroughbreds—Man o' War and Citation are perhaps the most famous—have made a great contribution to horse racing. They have also played a valuable role in breeding, by improving other strains and imparting their speed and stamina to them.

There has been much controversy—it goes back at least as far as the ancient Egyptians—as to whether a trotting horse ever has all its feet off the ground at one time. About 1875 or so, Leland Stanford bet twenty-five thousand dollars that a horse moving at full speed takes all four feet off the ground at the same time. He caused an English photographer, Eadweard Muybridge, to take a series of photographs of a horse in motion to prove the point. (Muybridge's invention for photographing the horse in motion, it is interesting to note in passing, was the basic idea that brought about motion pictures. Later Muybridge worked with Edison on the possibility of talking pictures.)

A handsome horse developed from the Thoroughbred group is the Hackney breed. Originally, about 1750, these horses were used for private carriages, but later on they were used for hackney cabs as well —hence our word "hacks". Today the Hackney breed has no practical value but it is still exhibited at horse shows.

The Quarter horse, one of America's most famous breeds, is descended from English horses brought to the Virginia colony in the days of Pocahontas and John Smith. For years the Quarter horse was the most popular type of race-horse in America. Later on, after the opening up of the West, the Quarter horse proved invaluable on cattle ranches. In recent years, the Quarter horse has been used a great deal as a saddle animal. Because of its outstanding intelligence and ready adaptability, this type often makes an admirable polo pony.

The Morgan horse, another popular, handsome American breed, which originated about 1800, is remarkably versatile. It began as a lowly farm horse, but soon came to be favoured as a saddle horse and then as an Army and police mount. Some of the finest trotting and harness racing horses have come from the Morgan breed.

Another breed that deserves mention is the American Saddle Horse, developed over a century ago in Kentucky. This handsome animal, with its even disposition, graceful carriage, and equable gait, is the favourite horse for pleasure-riding in the United States.

Fox hunting, traditionally an aristocratic sport, calls for horses of exceptional stamina and agility. Such horses are known as "Hunters", but they do not belong to any special breed. Long, patient training is required to develop the ability of these animals to jump over ditches and fences. Horses bred for steeplechase racing need even more rigorous training, for it is often literally true that their rider's life depends on them.

Polo is the sport that makes the sharpest demands on a horse's skill, intelligence, and adaptability.

Handsomest of all horses, it has been said, are the Palominos, with their predominantly golden colour. Though not a specific breed, they monopolize attention at shows and fairs because of their good looks. The flowing, flaxen mane and tail, setting off the rich, golden, bronze, or yellow coat diluted with various shades of chestnut or sorrel, is most pleasing to the eye.

WILD HORSES—DESTINED FOR EXTINCTION

Przewalski's Horse, or the Tarpan, *Equus przewalskii,* is the only wild horse left on earth today. True, there are many so-called "wild" horses in different parts of the world. However, with the exception of the tarpan, they are all descendants of domestic animals that have escaped from captivity.

SOLE SURVIVOR OF AN EXTINCT BREED

Scientifically speaking, a wild horse is not wild simply because it is found in an untamed state and resists capture and saddling. Such a horse is, more likely, the descendant of a domestic horse that escaped from captivity and went wild in its habits. In historic times a true wild horse has never been domesticated or bred by man, and the only one left in the world is Przewalski's Horse, pictured above. Quite different from the modern horses we know, this hardy creature has a small body and a large head with a prominent muzzle. The animal appears to be intermediate between the true horses and asses.

Przewalski's horse first came to the notice of zoologists when the explorer after whom it is named brought back a skin and skull from his Asiatic journeys. The animal is a sturdy, comparatively small pony that stands about four feet at the shoulder. It has a rather large head, small ears, and heavy jaws and teeth. The mane is short and erect, but the tail is long-haired all the way. The summer coat is reddish brown with some white about the muzzle; in winter, the coat is longer and paler.

The range of Przewalski's horse is limited to the plains of the Altai Mountains region and extreme western Mongolia. In April or May, probably eleven months after mating time, the mares are ready to foal. At this time they retreat to quiet places where food and water are plentiful.

Przewalski's horse will interbreed freely with "wild" ponies of the region, and hybrids are not uncommon.

THE HORSE FAMILY

The horse family is made up of asses and zebras as well as horses. Named after the horse—*equus* in Latin—this family (Equidae) is remarkable for the development of the foot. In all these animals, the foot has been reduced to a single digit, originally the third toe. This toe is enclosed in a compact, horny hoof.

The ankle and wrist have been raised high off the ground, becoming the so-called "knee" and hock of a horse. Such animals are adapted for high speed on hard, solid ground. Their teeth, with high crowns that gradually push upward with wear, are specialized for grazing and grinding close, coarse grass.

These animals have a long tail of whiplike hair. They use it to disperse the usual host of house flies and green horse flies—and also the more serious pests like the gadfly, which punctures the skin and deposits its eggs under the surface.

The equines are sociable creatures, running in herds that may contain hundreds of individuals. They breed about every other year. Mares usually have a single foal, born in an advanced stage of development.

Its eyes are open and it is able to stand unsupported a few minutes after birth.

DONKEYS—USEFUL AND MUCH MALIGNED

The donkey, or domesticated ass, has an honourable history—the animal has served man well for many thousands of years. Derived from the Abyssinian or Somali Wild Ass, which is still in existence, the donkey was probably domesticated in the New Stone Age, some twelve thousand years ago. The name "ass" probably stems from the word *athon*, which is Hebrew for she-ass. "Donkey" is a nickname derived from the animal's supposed dun colour.

The ass has a shorter mane and shorter tail hair than the horse, and only the end half is provided with a brush. Of course its ears are much longer than those of a horse. Superior to the horse when it comes to carrying loads, the donkey is famous for its sure-footed negotiation of dangerously narrow mountain trails. Man has employed the donkey since time immemorial as a pack and draught animal. The Egyptians used it extensively in their monument-building as far back as 3,000 B.C.; they do not seem to have had horses until 1,900 B.C.

Despite its reputation for stubbornness and stupidity, the donkey has accomplished much of man's "dirty work" under singularly un-rewarding conditions and often savage treatment. A patient and long-suffering creature, it outlives the horse; the donkey has a life expectancy of from twenty-five to forty-seven years.

There is usually one foal at a time, about nine months after mating.

THE DONKEY IN BIBLICAL LORE AND LEGEND

The numerous Biblical references to the donkey indicate to us how extensively the animal was used in ancient times. Besides heavy farm work, it had such thankless tasks as turning irrigation machines and large millstones. The donkey was a saddle animal as well as a beast of burden. Great men and rulers travelled on an ass colt, and such a mount was a token of a peaceful journey; the horse was reserved for war.

Thus in the Gospels Jesus is depicted entering Jerusalem on the colt of an ass.

We all know how mighty Samson slew a thousand Philistines with the jawbone of an ass. Then there is the famous story of Balaam and how his mount fell down on beholding the angel of the Lord standing with sword in hand. Quick to anger, Balaam struck the beast. Thereupon "the Lord opened the mouth of the ass, and she said unto Balaam, 'What have I done unto thee, that thou hast smitten me three times?' "

A charming legend relates that none was admitted to the Ark unless invited by Noah. With the coming of the floods, the Devil saw that he was going to be cut off from mankind. When the time arrived for the ass to go on board, it was taken with a fit of obstinacy. Losing

patience, Noah struck the ass, crying out, "Enter, thou devil!" Needless
to say, the Devil accepted the "invitation".

WILD COUSIN OF THE DOMESTIC DONKEY

With its small ears, slender head, and long legs, the Asiatic wild ass looks more like a
horse than like man's wilful servant the domestic donkey. (That creature, incidentally,
is descended from African stock.) Swift of foot and sociable toward their own kind, the
wild asses are sometimes seen in large numbers on the deserts of Asia, where the scarcity
of water does not appear to inconvenience them. The animals show considerable curiosity
about man, but will seldom allow him to come very near.

MULES—ANIMALS WITH NO FUTURE

The mule is a cross between a male donkey (jackass) and a female
horse. Both sexes of the mule are almost always sterile. These hybrids
rarely gallop and have a feeble bray unlike the voice of either an ass or
horse. The cross between a male horse and a female donkey is known
as a "hinny". It is smaller and inferior to the mule.

Man has bred mules since prehistoric times. They have often been
used for military transport, being particularly valuable in mountain
warfare. Darwin tells us that troops of mules in South American
mountain regions are led by steady old mares. These *madrinas* ("grand-
mothers") carry a bell. The mules show great affection for the *madrina*
and it is almost impossible to separate them from her.

There is a quaint legend to account for the mule's inability to breed. It is said that when the Holy Family was about to travel into Egypt, St. Joseph chose a mule to carry them. However, the animal kicked Joseph and he became angry. He laid a curse upon the animal, to the effect that it should never have parents or descendants of its own kind.

WILD ASSES—METTLESOME CREATURES

There is a world of difference between the wild donkey or ass in its native desert and the domesticated breed. The wild ass moves with a spirited, high-actioned gait, trotting freely over the rocks and sand with the speed of a horse. It is frequently captured by Arabs. The donkeys are run down by fast dromedaries. Invariably, it is the foals that are caught; as for the adults, they gallop too far away over the boundless desert to be overtaken. Despite the arid nature of their surroundings, wild donkeys always seem to be in good condition, and their flesh is eaten by the people.

Like all members of the horse family, wild asses are sociable creatures; in Mongolia, herds of a thousand head have been recorded. At foaling time the herds break up, and the mares, often accompanied by a stallion, retire to sheltered pastures where there is access to water. Pairing takes place in September and lasts about a month. May and June is the time for foaling. Usually the mare has one foal; occasionally there are twins.

A Mongolian wild ass can travel at the rate of forty miles per hour for the first mile; thereafter, its speed drops to thirty-five miles per hour. It can average as much as sixteen miles per hour for a distance of thirty miles. Though wild asses need water at regular intervals, they can go for a long time between drinks.

The African Wild Donkey, or Somali Wild Ass, *Equus asinus somalicus*, is probably the stock from which the domesticated donkey was derived. A handsome, strongly built animal, it stands about four feet six inches at the shoulder. Unlike the Asiatic wild asses, it has very large, long ears and narrow feet. The African wild ass gives voice to the loud bray of the familiar donkey—a very different sound from the squeals and guttural blowing of the Asiatic asses. The general body colour is grey with white under-parts, relieved by a white muzzle, a white patch around the eye, a black stripe down the back and another across the shoulders.

Both the Nubian wild ass and the related Algerian wild ass are now extinct in the wild state. However, several local variants—the Sudan, Somali, and Red Sea wild asses—still exist in limited numbers. These African wild asses frequent low, stony hill country and bleak wastes. They have a reputation for great speed and sure-footedness in rough country.

OTHER WILD ASSES

The Mongolian Wild Ass, *Equus hemionus*, also known as the Chigetal or Dziggetai, is a typical desert animal, slightly smaller than its North African cousins and has smaller ears. It dwells in the arid regions east of the Altai Mountains to Transbaikalia and the central Gobi Desert. The general colour of the body is chestnut, varying from a greyish tone in the long winter coat to a more reddish shade as summer comes on.

The Onager, or Persian Wild Ass, known as the Ghorkhar in India, is somewhat smaller and more slender than the Mongolian wild ass. Its general colour varies from cinnamon brown in the summer coat to yellow brown in the winter coat. This animal lives in the desert regions from Persia and Syria to north-western India. It has a close relative in the wild ass of Baluchistan and western India, a comparatively light-coloured creature.

The Kiang, or Tibetan Wild Ass, the largest and most handsome of the Asiatic wild asses, ranges over the high mountain plateaus of Tibet at altitudes up to sixteen thousand feet. Except for its larger size and slightly different colour pattern it is much the same as the Mongolian wild ass.

ZEBRAS—AN OLD PUZZLE

The reader is doubtless familiar with the classic question about the zebra—is it a light-coloured animal with dark stripes, or a dark-coloured animal with light stripes? Here is the verdict of science: the colour pattern of the zebra consists of dark or black stripes on a light background. The animal, therefore, is white—or nearly white—with black stripes.

The attractively striped horselike animals that come under the popular name of zebra are the representatives of the horse family in eastern and southern Africa. Zebras resemble asses in having a short, erect mane, large ears, and a large head. In most zebras, the hoof is narrower than a horse's hoof, but broader and more rounded than an ass's hoof. The Mountain Zebra has the large ears of the Somali wild ass and similar small narrow feet.

MEAT FOR THE LION

The zebra is choice food for the lion—wherever zebras are present in abundance, there you will find lions as well. Once struck down by a lion a zebra makes little show of resistance and succumbs quickly, resigned to the inevitable.

Ordinarily quick with its heels, the zebra also has important offensive weapons in its teeth. Wild dogs and other flesh-eaters seldom attack it—always with the important exception of the lion. Luckily the zebra possesses several defences against the lion. It has a good sense of smell and excellent eyesight. The famous striped coat is helpful, for the stripes blend well with the shadows of branches against sunlight or moonlight.

Zebras drink regularly and are rarely more than five miles away from water. On their way to drink they are always on the alert for lions. They have no fixed time for drinking, but generally they approach a waterhole late in the evening or early in the morning. However, the author has seen zebras at a waterhole in the middle of the day.

A herd of zebras on their way to water are usually led by an old stallion; first galloping ahead, he pulls up short of the waterhole to look for lurking lions. Satisfied that the approach is safe, he gives the "all clear"—a low neigh—and the herd moves in to drink. They are always nervous and alert when drinking, as if expecting lions—and seem relieved when they get away from the water on to the open plains.

OTHER ENEMIES—MAN AND DISEASE

In recent years, large numbers of zebras have been killed for their hides—these make tough leather, suitable for military shoes and equipment. Sportsmen often shoot zebras when other game is scarce. During epidemics of cattle disease, zebras die by the thousands. Fortunately they are sufficiently numerous to quickly fill in their depleted ranks—

otherwise the lions would be obliged to turn their attention to domestic cattle and hunt man, too, more often than they do.

ZEBRA HERDS

During their migrations, zebras travel in large herds, sometimes over a thousand in number. It is not easy to imagine a more awe-inspiring sight than a herd of these ornately marked horses thundering through the forest.

Like many other animals, zebras seem possessed with a desire to overtake a motor-car. On one occasion in East Africa a herd raced up alongside the author's hunting car and crossed in front of him. It took the herd nearly fifteen minutes to pass, travelling at full gallop,

ITS BRILLIANT STRIPES ARE ACTUALLY PROTECTIVE

In wooded areas, the celebrated black and white stripes of the zebra merge with sunlight and shadow to create a natural camouflage. But protective coloration alone will not always fool the zebra's mighty and persistent foe, the lion. To help it elude the stalking big cat, the zebra relies upon its highly developed senses of hearing and of smell. Perhaps the most beautiful stripes of all are found on the mountain zebra, above, which has intricate horizontal markings on its hind parts.

four or five abreast. Most of the time there were no breaks in the fast-moving procession. Once on the other side of the trail, they vanished into the forest.

A CLOSER LOOK AT THE ZEBRAS

There are three kinds of zebras living today, and one extinct variety. Grevy's Zebra is the largest and one of the most elegant of the striped ponies. It stands four feet six inches at the shoulder and weighs between five hundred and seven hundred pounds. The entire head and body are finely lined. Grevy's zebra lives in the open brush-covered plains and in the lowlands of Abyssinia, Somaliland, and northern Kenya. The mare is just as big as the stallion.

Burchell's Zebra or Bontequagga, the common broad-striped zebra of Africa, dwells in most of the southern and eastern parts of the continent, where it frequents open plains, hills, and lightly forested country. This small-eared animal stands four feet two inches at the shoulder. The Mountain Zebra, the smallest of the striped ponies, is the most asslike of all, and perhaps the most attractively marked. It is confined to the mountains of South Africa.

The Quagga is now extinct; the last living individual died in 1872 in the London Zoo. Originally found in herds on the open plains of the Cape Colony, the quagga differed greatly in colour and pattern of marking from Burchell's zebra. Nevertheless, the two animals are believed to have been closely related.

Essentially grass-eaters, zebras are fond of lightly forested country. They reach their maximum in brilliance and colour pattern in the wooded portions of Central and East Africa. South and westward, as the forests thin out and the region becomes more arid, there is a gradual weakening of the striping. In the quagga of the south the stripes were dark brown and restricted to the neck and head. Zebras love to take dust baths and sand baths, and zebra country is full of well-worn rolling grounds.

The zebra's first burst of speed is remarkable; for more sustained running, it is credited with a speed of forty miles per hour, as timed by a car speedometer. The zebra has been domesticated and driven in harness for exhibition purposes, but it is not to be trusted. It is stubborn and tires quickly when put to work.

Life expectancy for zebras in the natural state is about fifteen years, but they have lived as long as twenty-nine years in captivity. There appears to be no fixed breeding season, and the young are born between eleven and thirteen months after mating.

UNDERSTANDING THE ODD-TOED HOOFED MAMMALS

As we have seen, the horse family is made up of asses and zebras in addition to horses. But the horse family is only part of a larger group, the order of odd-toed hoofed mammals. This order, known as Perissodactyla ("odd-fingered"), also includes tapirs and rhinoceroses. The order has no representatives in Europe, in the Americas north of southern Mexico, or in Australia. The tapir, the only member of the order alive today in the New World, is not found in Africa.

Representatives of this order are not "ruminants"—they do not chew their cud. They have front teeth in both upper and lower jaws and, with the exception of the rhinoceros, do not have antlers or horns.

An interesting point about the odd-toed hoofed mammals is this: when scientists gave the animals this name, they used the term "odd-toed" to refer to the *structure* of the foot, not the *number* of toes. These mammals have an enlarged third toe, which extends up into the main leg-bone and bears all or a large portion of the weight of the body. This is especially true of the horse family, which has only one toe, and also applies to the other animals of the order, which have more than one toe. (Of course, whatever the number of toes, they are encased in a hoof.) As you will see in later pages, there are other hoofed mammals that rest the weight of the body on *two* toes. We call them even-toed hoofed mammals.

One of the biggest of the rhinoceroses, the great Indian rhinoceros, has a mild, quiet disposition compared with his highly excitable African black relative. The Indian rhinoceros may weigh three tons and is distinguished by its heavily folded studded skin and its single horn.   *See page 675*

[6-5]

[6-5A]

"Hippopotamus" literally means "river horse" but by virtue of being even-toed, the hippo is scientifically classified with the pigs. Vying with the rhino for second place in size among land animals, the hippo is equally vegetarian, its precision-ground boarlike tusks being particularly well suited for shearing reeds and grasses.   *See page 692*

[6-6]

Wild pigs in general are mentally alert and decisive in action and the largest of them, the Eurasian wild boar, is no exception. A strong, sinewy creature possessed of great courage, it can be extremely dangerous at bay.

See page 682

[6-6A]

Slightly smaller, but still a giant in the pig family, the African forest hog is such a secretive animal that it was not discovered until 1904. Very little authentic information is available concerning its habits and history. *See page 687*

The nearest the American continents come to having a "native" pig is the peccary, a gregarious animal closely related to the true pigs but differing from them in scientifically important small details.

See page 691

[6-6B]

TAPIRS—STRANGE, PRIMITIVE, TIMID, AND INOFFENSIVE

When you compare it with the highly specialized mammals of the modern age, you can see that the tapir is a strange, primitive creature. Its snout and upper lip are lengthened into a short, thick, flexible trunk that is used to draw twigs and branches into the mouth. It is a stockily built animal, with short legs and a plump, thick-skinned body covered with short, close hair. Its tail is a mere few inches long; the eyes are small, and the ears, of medium length, extend out and up from the sides of the head.

The tapir has four toes on the front feet, and three on the hind feet. The third toe, as we have seen in the case of the horse family, is the central axis of the foot. The tapir, the only living odd-toed hoofed mammal native to the Americas, can spread its toes.

The tapirs of today are the last of a great race that all but vanished in geological time. Eventually they were left on opposite sides of the earth, without connecting links. The prehistoric tapirs were spread across the Northern Hemisphere, but today we find these animals only in the Malayan region of southern Asia and in two parts of the New World: Central America and northern South America. They have a distinct family all to themselves, the Tapiridae.

RELIC OF A PREHISTORIC AGE

The tapir, strange-looking and primitive, gives us a good living picture of a prehistoric animal. Its body reminds us of the pig, and its snout and upper lip are elongated.

Timid, inoffensive creatures, tapirs live in swamps or near water-courses. Taking readily to the water, they are said to be able to dive and walk along the river floor. Tapirs feed on water plants and browse on forest foliage. Active only at night for the most part, they are more or less solitary; no more than two or three individuals are ever seen together. Tapirs have no fixed breeding season. Usually one offspring is produced; twins are rare.

Taken young, the tapir is quite docile and can even be expected to return if it is permitted to roam in the forest by itself. In South and Central America its only natural enemy is the jaguar; in Malaya the tiger and leopard assume this role. It fights hard if cornered and can usually escape if it has access to the water.

SOUTH AMERICAN TAPIRS—FIGHTERS AND SWIMMERS

The South American Tapir, *Tapirus terrestris*, dwells in the warmer parts of South America, with a range extending from Panama to Argentina, Bolivia, and Paraguay. This blackish-brown animal is common in the forests of the Guianas, Venezuela, and Brazil, where the natives hunt it with the help of trained dogs. If pursued it kicks violently—it may seize a hound in its teeth and shake it furiously.

In the Wild. The tapir does not always follow a beaten trail, as most animals do; more often it doggedly pushes its way through the jungle with its head carried low.

Leo E. Miller, writing of his experiences at Mt. Duida, Brazil, says: "I saw them moving singly through the forest and fording the shallow Rio Sina like shadows, so quietly did they move." Disturb them and they crash through the forest at a quick trot and even gallop. In their stomachs Miller found mostly palm nuts with seeds the size of hen's eggs. The pulp surrounding the seeds had been digested but the large hard seeds were intact.

In the Water. Theodore Roosevelt hunted tapirs on the Sepotuba River ("river of tapirs" in the local Indian dialect) of the Matto Grosso in Brazil. He noted that, when pursued, they always take to the water, wherever it is available. He saw a large male swimming with only its strange head above the surface; when diving, it curled its trunk under. Swimming rapidly downstream, it stayed under water for an astonishingly long time after diving. It passed completely under his dugout canoe, and came up on the opposite side halfway between him and the river bank.

A tapir shot in the water always goes to the bottom; but in about an hour the body will rise to the surface.

In Captivity. Captured young, the South American tapir quickly becomes tame. However, it does not respond to kindness and shows little interest in anyone. Give it a place to sleep and food to eat and it is satisfied with its lot; it seems to have no inclination to leave the shelter of a comfortable home. It is not apt to bite; when the animal is molested, a shrill hissing cry is the extent of its anger. The tapir has a gluttonous appetite and in captivity will devour almost anything—raw meat or even rags.

The tapir's flesh is considered excellent and is often used as food. Natives believe they can cure epilepsy by grinding down the creature's toenails and taking them in powdered form.

OTHER INTERESTING TAPIRS

The Mountain Tapir, or Pinchaque, *Tapirus roulini,* dwells in the mountain forest of Ecuador and Colombia up to elevations of eight thousand feet. It has a rounded head and is covered with coarse blackish hair about an inch long.

This animal gets its scientific name from Désiré Roulin, a doctor and zoologist, who accompanied Jean Baptiste Boussingault, the illustrious French scientist, from 1824 to 1827 on his Andean explorations. While crossing the bare mountain heights of the Andes in Colombia, Roulin came across this strange-looking animal, which resembles the typical South American tapir but has long, thick hair like a bear's. Roulin made a remarkable drawing of the creature, which has since been published.

The Central American Tapir ranges from southern Mexico to Panama, from sea-level up to six thousand feet in the mountains. While the adult is uniformly blackish brown in colour, its throat, chest, and face are more or less whitish. The head-and-body length comes to six feet five inches; the tail is only three inches long. A large male may weigh up to six hundred pounds.

The Malay Tapir lives in the Malay Peninsula and north as far as Tenasserim, Burma. It stands three and one-half feet at the shoulder and weighs about five hundred pounds. Its colour is partly a soiled whitish, partly black or blackish.

Rhinoceroses—Temperamental Behemoths

THE RHINOCEROS, a huge, ungainly creature, is actually, or comes close to being, the second largest of all land mammals (the elephant is the biggest; the hippo vies with the rhino for second place).

Consequently, it is hard for our minds to accept the fact that the rhinoceros, sizable as it is, can be considered only a miniature compared to one of its ancestors. Millions of years ago *Baluchitherium*, a hornless rhinoceros, had its heyday. This giant of central Asia stood seventeen feet nine inches at the shoulder and measured thirty-four feet from the tip of its big nose to the end of its tail!

Even so, the rhinoceros is no midget. Its great bulk renders it practically immune to attack by lions, tigers, and other natural enemies. We might think, then, that the rhinoceros would be a contented, not to say complacent, creature. Not so!—though generally non-aggressive, to be sure, this hulking mammal is surly and unreliable in temper. When suddenly confronted with danger, it is apt to charge without provocation. Given time to digest the situation, it will usually seek safety in flight.

Why does the rhinoceros tend to charge on sudden impulse? We do not quite know. It has fairly acute senses of smell and hearing, but its eyesight is none too good and, if the truth must be told, it is not particularly bright. Perhaps the headlong dash of the rhinoceros is instinctive, handed down from an age when the flesh-eaters were more powerful and less discriminating when scanning the bill of fare. (The rhinoceros itself is a strict vegetarian, limited to green foliage, grasses, and the like.)

At any rate, some present-day observers believe that the precipitate rush of the rhino may be due to curiosity, or perhaps its nearsightedness. Others claim that the animal is anxious to protect its young.

Today we find rhinoceroses only in the warmer parts of Africa and Asia and in Indonesia. But these behemoths, survivors of a bygone age (we place them with the horses and tapirs in the order of odd-toed hoofed mammals) when armed might was a determining factor in survival, once ranged over the entire Northern Hemisphere. The woolly rhinoceros, a prehistoric creature that lived millions of years ago in northern Europe and Asia along with the woolly mammoth, has been discovered in a remarkably good state of preservation, frozen in the Arctic ice. This find was unearthed in Siberia in 1731.

MEET MR. RHINO

The rhinoceros is a great, clumsy beast protected by a thick, scantily haired hide. Its legs are on the stubby side and its three-toed feet are shod with a broad, horny, compact sole. Its massive head is concave in front.

This head is armed with one or two horns that continue to grow throughout the rhino's life. We might plausibly suppose that the horn is connected to the skull by means of a bony core. The fact is, though, that the horn is merely an outgrowth of the skin, and is composed of a well-consolidated mass of hair. It is the horns that give these creatures their family name (Rhinocerotidae—"nose horns").

SEEING-EYE OF THE SHORT-SIGHTED RHINO

The rhinoceros is considered a good swimmer. It loves to wallow in mud and bathe in dust to rid itself of ticks and other skin parasites. Some birds make a practice of picking over the head or back of the animal, and are even enterprising enough to enter the rhino's ears in search of these insect pests. Tick birds also act as lookouts, giving warning of approaching intruders by their noisy, scolding chatter.

Incidentally, what was probably the first rhinoceros seen in Europe was advertised in the *London Gazette* in 1684. It was brought by East Indian merchants, and sold for two thousand pounds.

BLACK RHINOCEROSES— AFRICA'S COMMONEST

The African Black or Hook-lipped Rhinoceros, *Diceros bicornis* ("two horned"), is the common species of Africa. Standing five feet at the shoulders, a full-grown male may weigh as much as three thousand pounds. Its upper lip, extended into a point, is prehensile for grasping twigs and leaves and drawing them into the mouth.

This rhino, as we can tell from its name, has two horns; it sometimes happens that females have longer horns than the males. As a rule, the front horn is the longer of the two, the record length being fifty-three and one-half inches. The average length, however, is about half that much.

There is no doubt that the black rhino has an excellent notion of local geography, and a sense of smell that is keen without being on a par with the elephant's or the buffalo's. Likewise its sense of hearing serves it well; but when it comes to vision, this animal, like all its cousins, scarcely sees any better than a nearsighted man without his glasses.

The African natives kill the black rhinoceros with their elephant spears. (Interestingly enough, they fear it nowhere near as much as they do the elephant.) The rhino's tough hide, one-half to three-quarters of an inch thick, makes splendid fighting shields; the natives bleach it almost white. As for the rhino's flesh, it is, as you might expect, coarse grained and rather tough. However, the Africans pound it with stones till it becomes fairly palatable. They consider the liver a great delicacy.

A DAY WITH THE RHINO

The black or hook-lipped rhinoceros usually has a home territory about ten miles in diameter. Inside this area there must be a water hole or other drinking place. If the water dries up, the beast will find a fresh supply somewhere else. It usually goes for a drink about midnight, but there is no fixed time. Although early morning and evening are the times of greatest activity, the black rhino may be abroad any hour of the day or night. It is an unsociable creature, and it is a rare occasion when we find more than two or three individuals (including a calf) together.

There was a time when the black rhinoceros was common over most of Africa south of the Sahara; today it is plentiful only in East

Africa. Though steep, rocky hill country is the ideal habitat for this animal, the author has often seen it on the plains. Like other members of its family, this rhino makes a ritual of rolling in the dry dust bowls. It is never so happy as when wallowing in soft, wet mud. Narrow, winding trails of the rhino lead in all directions from the wallow back into the bush.

THE RHINOCEROS HAS AN UNPREDICTABLE TEMPER

Though it often behaves peaceably enough, the rhinoceros is untrustworthy, and given to sudden temperamental flare-ups; for no apparent reason, it may rush forward in a fierce attack. The African black or hook-lipped rhinoceros, pictured above, will frequently become enraged by the scent of man and charge at him. The animal is capable of a speed of thirty miles or more per hour.

Primarily a browser, the rhino feeds on the shoots and leaves of low bushes; it is also partial to twigs, as well as herbage and some long grasses. It does most of its feeding during the early morning, late evening and night. Its droppings are usually deposited in saucer-like hollows which have been scooped out under a tree or bush. Not infrequently a great pile accumulates. One may observe trails extending from one dumping place to another; deep crescent-shaped furrows are ploughed in the ground around these toilets.

The black rhino does most of its sleeping in some shady spot during the heat of the day. It slumbers in various positions—one animal was found fast asleep standing up, others have been seen sleeping on their sides, or with feet doubled up under the body. Some rhinos get up front feet first, like a horse; others rise hind legs first like a cow.

THE RHINO'S IMPETUOUS CHARGES

Suddenly startled, a rhino will snort like a horse. If it is really frightened, it lets out a shrill squeal. The black rhino is one of the few animals that will charge man without the slightest provocation. What causes this inherited animosity toward man is, as we have seen, a matter for debate. Whatever the cause, charge they will if you come upon them suddenly in the bush.

On one occasion, two full-grown rhinos charged at the author's hunting car from two directions. First they came on with heads carried high and then lowered them for a conclusive thrust, their murderous spiked horns directed straight ahead. At the critical moment, the author's "white hunter" fired his rifle. A perfect hit square on the horn swung one of the animals around so that it charged into its comrade and so saved the day.

Despite such occasional encounters, most of these animals turn and run at the approach of man. A rhino usually stampedes upwind—if you are in its line of travel, it will charge at you. But if you are downwind, the chances are it will not get your scent. The odour of the human body is a hateful stench in the nostrils of the rhino, as it is to most other wild game, but, as we have indicated, this does not necessarily alone explain the animal's anger.

Despite its short legs and great body, the rhinoceros can keep abreast of a car going twenty-eight miles per hour. Charging, the animal can do thirty-five miles per hour. Just as we would expect, it is not quick in turning, and it is easy to dodge a charging rhino—if you do not get panic-stricken.

There is one creature to which the rhino always courteously concedes the right of way—the elephant. The chances are that it has learned from long experience to respect its formidable associate of the African veldt.

CATCHING RHINOS AMERICAN STYLE

"Buffalo" Jones, the famous American cowboy, once lassoed a full-grown black rhino in Africa and finally succeeded in capturing it. Time and again, when the animal was roped, it dragged the horses from several directions until the lines snapped. Using his three horses in relays, Jones was gradually able to tire out the rhinoceros. Still, the horses were only slightly faster than the rhino, and they had many a narrow escape from the persistent charges of the infuriated beast. Eventually a lasso around a hind leg held the now exhausted animal and it was tethered to a tree.

In later days, museum expeditions have lassoed rhinos from a moving truck. Sometimes the lasso is attached to a heavy log which goes to the ground as the animal pulls. After the rhino has worn itself out pulling the log, it is more easily captured.

LOVE AMONG THE RHINOS

In his book, *Big Game Hunting and Adventure*, Marcus Daly tells an interesting story about the love life of the black rhinoceros. One moonlit night he was watching a bull and cow standing motionless, a few yards apart. Suddenly the cow rushed around the bull at a fast pace. Then, as a climax to the dance, she jumped high in the air, came down flat on the ground, skidded along on her throat, rose, shook herself, and took up her original position facing the bull.

Now it was her mate's turn. Wheeling around and around his lady friend in a most amazing manner, often spinning like a top on sharp turns but never changing his course, he finally did the high jump and came to rest after skidding a considerable distance on his throat. When he got up, they alternated through the whole procedure for half an hour. At that point, thoroughly exhausted by their exertions, they went off for a drink, disappearing into the African night.

There is no fixed mating season for the black rhino. Reproduction is slow in this family, the young being born about eighteen months after mating time. There is usually one calf, weighing about seventy-five pounds. After a few hours, it is able to follow its mother around. But though the calf is quick to obtain the mother's care, it is slow to relinquish it. The youngster is suckled for about two years, and continues to stay with her until more than half grown. The mother will not mate again while she has a calf with her.

The life expectancy of the black rhino in the wild state is probably not over twenty-five years. A captive animal lived to the age of forty-seven.

WHITE RHINOCEROSES—BIGGEST OF THE TRIBE

The White Rhinoceros, or Burchell's Rhinoceros, *Ceratotherium simum*, is also known as the square-lipped rhinoceros. It is the biggest of all the rhinos. Standing six and one-half feet at the shoulder, the white rhino weighs up to four tons. Despite its bulk, this giant, like the elephant, has an uncanny knack of slipping silently away, even in dense thickets.

Among the white rhinos, both sexes have two horns, the front one being about twice the length of the rear one. It is not unusual for the front horn to measure three feet in length; the recorded maximum is five feet.

WHITE BUT NOT QUITE

Actually, the colour of the white rhino's hide is smoky grey. View it by bright moonlight on the grassy plains, however, and the animal really appears white; so perhaps its name is not so inappropriate as many highly critical observers have claimed. In any event, the normal tone of the skin is somewhat obscured by the colour of the mud in which the rhinoceros wallows ecstatically.

A FAIRLY GOOD-TEMPERED RHINO

The white rhinoceros seems mild tempered and slow compared to its more nervous and highly irascible black relative; and it is correspondingly less likely to charge blindly at a possible foe. It is more sociable, too. White rhinos frequently gather in parties that include a bull, a cow, and calves of assorted ages.

When feeding, the white rhinoceros moves slowly upwind as it grazes during the cool early morning and evening hours; during the heat of the day it slumbers peacefully under the ample shade of a tree. When disturbed, this ungainly beast makes off at a swift trot, its nose close to the ground. Pressed for speed, it will break into a gallop and keep up a fast pace for quite a distance.

YOUNG RHINOS

It is estimated that the female white rhino has her baby about seventeen or eighteen months after mating time. Slow as this rate of breeding is, it is faster than the black rhino's. Occasionally a cow will have twins, but such instances are rare. A calf is mature at about five or six years, and is then ready to breed.

Unlike the black rhino's calf, which tags along behind its mother, the white rhino's calf precedes the cow. The youngster is steered in the right direction by the pressure of the maternal horns on its rump. When a cow, accompanied by its young, is shot, the calf will charge the intruder—just as the baby elephant does in the same pitiful plight.

WHERE THEY LIVE

Today the white rhinoceros dwells in a comparatively limited region in Central Africa. Formerly common on the grassy prairies of South Africa, this rhinoceros had been practically eliminated there at the turn of the century, with a few survivors left to enjoy the protection of the game preserve in Zululand, Natal. Strangely enough, there are no white rhinos in the area lying between the northern and southern limits of its range.

THE GREAT INDIAN RHINOCEROS

The Great Indian Rhinoceros, or One-horned Rhinoceros, *Rhinoceros unicornis*, is the largest rhino found in Asia. A big male may stand slightly more than five and one-half feet at the shoulder and weigh about two tons or more. These creatures haunt the great plains of northern India, Assam, and Nepal, where the giant grass grows to a height of fifteen or twenty feet. Here the Indian rhino lives among the grassy runways like an enormous field mouse!

Both male and female are equipped with a single horn. It rarely exceeds a foot in length—though some rare specimens measure up to twenty-four inches.

AN "IRON-PLATED RHINOCEROS"

The Indian rhino's thick hide is folded into plates or shields, hinged at the joints and studded with small rounded lumps which—by a slight stretch of your imagination—can pass for rivet heads. This beast is often described as the "iron-plated rhinoceros", and, imaginatively speaking, it does look as if it had been put together in a machine shop. The skin, dark grey in colour, is practically hairless—apart from a fringe on the ears and at the end of the tail.

VICIOUS TEMPERS

The Indian rhinoceros is likely to show extraordinary fits of temper without the least provocation. At such times it rushes about, uttering loud grunts, trampling down the bush, and cutting deep furrows in the ground with its horn. In the course of one of those seemingly meaningless displays of anger, it will furiously assault any moving object.

THE RHINOCEROS HAS A "MAGICAL" HORN

The great Indian or one-horned rhinoceros is esteemed by the natives because of a superstitious belief that its horn will act as an aphrodisiac or an antidote to poison. The horn, though hard, is actually a clump of hairs held together by an adhesive substance; dissolved or made into a powder, it brings a high price throughout the Far East. Museums in the Orient must take precautions to protect their rhinoceros specimens from the natives.

Even large bull elephants are not safe from the violence of this ill-tempered beast, and in the ferocious battle that ensues, a big tusker may acknowledge defeat and make a hurried retreat. In such duels the rhino is more likely to slash with its teeth than strike with its horn —the teeth are more effective weapons against the elephant's tough hide.

The female rhinoceros, despite these occasional ugly outbursts, is all sweetness toward her calf and very solicitous for its welfare. In the midst of her protective fury against intruders, she may suddenly decide that discretion is the better part of maternal care, and prudently lead her calf to safety in flight.

The young rhino is born about eighteen or nineteen months after its parents have mated. A newborn calf is about two feet high at the shoulder and weighs between seventy-five and 120 pounds. Born in a very advanced stage of development, the youngster is able to follow its mother soon after birth. One Indian rhino lived to the age of fifty in a zoo.

A FAMOUS RHINO SUPERSTITION

In India, many superstitions centre about the rhinoceros horn and its supposed exceptional medicinal qualities. (Europe once talked the same way about the unicorn's horn.) The most celebrated of its virtues, so it is held, is that the horn is an antidote against poison. The horn is used in treating a victim of poisoning—it is even used to detect the presence of poison!

For centuries, Indian rulers have drunk from cups made of rhinoceros horn, in the belief that this substance "sweats" on contact with poison. Such cups, mounted in silver or gold, are considered appropriate gifts for the highest dignitaries. Science can give no comfort to these beliefs; actual experiment with various poisons has elicited no reaction from the horn.

OTHER EASTERN RHINOS

The Javan or Lesser One-horned Rhinoceros, *Rhinoceros sondaicus*, reminds us in many ways of its great Indian cousin. However, the Javan variety is more slender and smaller, with a shoulder height of about four feet six inches, and a weight of over a ton. It has only one horn, which may be as much as ten inches long in the male. A few females are hornless; most have a very small horn.

The Javan rhino's skin is cracked into a mosaic pattern of scalelike discs, and the folds on the foreshoulder meet over the back of the lower neck. These folds in the Indian rhino curve backward toward the rear of the shoulder and do not meet.

Originally found in Burma, Assam, Indo-China, and through the Malay Peninsula to Sumatra and Java, the Javan rhino has been exterminated over most of its former range. It favours thick jungle and marshland, but it has also been found in forested mountain country.

The Sumatran or Asiatic Two-horned Rhinoceros, *Dicerorhinus sumatrensis*, is the smallest of the living rhinos, rarely exceeding one ton in weight and four and one-half feet in shoulder height. This animal has two horns, one in line behind the other. The front one is the larger of the pair, reaching a length of fifteen or twenty inches in the male. The rear horn, placed between the eyes, is seldom more than seven inches long. The female's horns are smaller.

The Sumatran rhino often goes by the name of "the hairy rhinoceros" —the hair is hard to see but can easily be felt by hand. The newborn are covered with thick brown hair, which disappears in time.

Like the Javan rhinoceros, this beast frequents thick forest and bamboo country, where it leaves well-worn trails between wallows. Today the Sumatran rhino dwells in Sumatra, Borneo, and the Malay Peninsula.

Porkers and River-Horses—
Pigs, Peccaries, and Hippopotamuses

HAVE YOU ever observed a pig's snout? It is more remarkable than might be supposed from a casual glance. The snout acts as a combination steam shovel and bulldozer—it is used to lift and push weights, to dig, and to break through tangled undergrowth.

Such tasks call for an exceptionally durable organ, and the pig's snout answers that description well. At the end of the long, flexible muzzle the nostrils open on a tough, flat, mobile, disclike plate. This is reinforced within by gristle attached to the skull.

As for the pig's mouth, it is noteworthy for the razor-keen tusks in particular. Usually—not always—the pair in the upper jaw are larger and curl upward. They are kept sharp by the honing action as they rub against the tusks of the lower jaw.

Wild pigs are mentally alert and decisive in action. The ground is their native element—they don't climb trees; however, they can swim. They are sociable and love company. Living in forests or bush country, they depend largely on roots and tubers for food. But they also eat small animal life, fruits, nuts, berries, and the like.

Pigs are creatures of temperate and warm regions. We find them well distributed over the Eastern Hemisphere, including Madagascar, but not Australia. In the Western Hemisphere, the hog family is represented by the peccaries.

Extinct pigs, some of them gigantic, lived in Europe during the Pliocene age, which ended over a million years ago, after lasting about eleven million years. Man tamed some of their smaller descendants at an early date; in China we have found bones of domestic pigs in New Stone Age sites, and the chances are that the Chinese domestication of the pig goes back well into prehistoric times.

Among domestic pigs, the Razorback Hogs of the south-eastern

United States and the Diving Pigs of the Florida islands have reverted to the wild type; and we find such "feral" pigs on many of the islands of the West Indies as well.

In the old days of sailing ships, salt pork was an important item on the menu of any vessel. The flesh of the pig absorbs salt more readily than most other kinds of meat and can therefore be preserved longer. Then, too, it is a plentiful and inexpensive kind of meat, for pigs are great breeders. Domestic sows may have as many as two, and sometimes even three, litters of young in a single year. The piglets may number anywhere from eight to twenty-two, and it is to be noted that the sow has more teats than any other animal—she may possess up to twenty-eight. Among the wild pigs, too, some types tend to large families.

WILD PIGS OF EUROPE AND ASIA

THE EURASIAN WILD BOAR—IT PITS ITS STRENGTH AGAINST MAN'S

The Eurasian Wild Boar, *Sus scrofa*, is a rugged, sinewy creature. It is a forester, and is especially useful in breaking up the tangled mass of roots and excess growth on the forest floor and freeing timber from the stranglehold of vines and brush. Another way in which this animal is of great value is that its bristles are manufactured into the finest utility paint brushes.

That, of course, is a far cry from the living animal. The Eurasian wild boar, in life, presents a most impressive appearance. It is the largest of all the wild pigs. Standing over three feet at the shoulder, it has a head-and-body length of almost five feet; a large boar weighs 350 pounds, sometimes even more. In colour it is dusky or greyish brown. Its coat is made up of long, coarse, black hair that overlays the thick, woolly, yellowish-brown underfur. The large, sharp, strong tusks may be almost a foot long.

(The word "boar", by the way, is apt to prove confusing, as it can be employed in two senses. We say of all pigs that the male is a "boar" and the female is a "sow". But the term "wild boar" refers universally to a species, male and female, and that is the way it is used here.)

Boar-Hunting—a Popular Sport. Hunting the Eurasian wild boar with spears and dogs was an immensely popular sport during the

[6-7]   The naturalist who 200 years ago called the potto the most disagreeable looking
animal on earth apparently never saw a wart hog: this unfortunate beast seems
to be the repository for every repulsive feature imaginable. Although it can
occasionally be seen grazing with zebras and antelope on the African plains,
it is a true pig and usually "roots" for vegetable growth just under the surface
of the ground.   *See page 688*

The llama, domesticated by Peruvian Indians some 3,000 years ago, still serves South America as a valuable beast of burden in rugged terrain at high altitudes. Depending upon their size, llamas can carry loads ranging from 65 to 200 pounds, but should an individual feel himself overloaded he will simply sit down and refuse to move.   *See page 703*

[6-8]

[6-8A]

The Bactrian or two-humped camel of Central Asia is further distinguished from its one-humped relative of the North African desert country by the long shaggy hair which protects it from the colder climate of its habitat. Also, with shorter legs and heavier build, it is slower but stronger.
See page 700

Middle Ages, and it flourished in England. In some parts of Europe and India the pastime still lives on today.

Courageous and ferocious when held at bay, this magnificent animal is more than a match for a whole pack of hounds. It will unhesitatingly charge a hunter mounted on horseback, and many a sportsman has been seriously scarred or killed in a desperate encounter with one of these diehard fighters. Old English writers referred to the sport with justice as "a verie dangerous exercise".

OBJECT OF MANY A THRILLING HUNT

Before the age of guns, hunting the European wild boar was a great and dangerous challenge to hunters. A fierce and fearless animal, the wild boar would turn and charge both the mounted huntsman and his horse, often wounding or killing them. Today, the wild boar can be easily shot down. The animal has its practical uses—its strong, stiff bristles end up in paint-brushes.

Because of the hazards involved, killing the wild boar ranked as a deed of chivalry during the Middle Ages. The animals, which are recorded as living in the neighbourhood of London in 1174, continued to be numerous in England until the improvement in firearms made it comparatively easy to kill them.

It was the custom for a pack of hounds and men mounted on horseback to take part in the chase. Brought to bay, an old stager would rush its assailants with great ferocity, and was almost certain to wound one or more of the dogs. The horses were also likely to be ripped

EAL/6—E

about the legs and their riders thrown to the ground; then the infuriated beast would charge the unfortunate horseman before he could rise. In such crucial instances the punctilio of the sport permitted the use of firearms. (The orthodox manner of ending the hunt, if all went well —for the hunters, that is—was for one of them to plunge his knife into the throat of the charging boar.)

That the killing of a wild boar is not always a quick and sure job, even when guns are used, the author has seen for himself. Once, when he was in Iran, camping on the shores of the Caspian Sea, a native sent a runner asking for help in getting rid of a wild boar that was devastating his vegetable garden. (Being a Mohammedan, the native could not slay the animal himself.) After driving about twenty miles, the author came to the man's cottage at dusk and shot the animal, which seemingly fell dead.

The big boar was loaded on to the front bumper of the writer's car and he and his party began to drive back to their camp in the dark. Imagine everyone's amazement when suddenly the stillness was rent by a hair-raising scream that came from somewhere in front of the radiator. It took a few seconds to realize that the "dead" boar had all of a sudden come to life. The next few minutes were hectic, but the maddened animal was finally subdued.

Boar's Head and Roasted Sucking Pig. The killing of a wild boar and the serving of its head at Christmas in "Merrie England" dates back to the ancient custom of making a boar offering to the goddess Freya at the winter solstice. In those days, people worshipped the boar as a symbol of fertility of the land, and hunted and killed it with colourful pageantry. The English custom of eating a roasted sucking pig on feast-days is a survival of these ancient ceremonies.

A Prolific Breeder. The Eurasian wild boar is prolific; there are likely to be two litters a year, with four to six babies in each. After mingling with the sows during the mating periods, the males then separate into small bands by themselves. When "pigging" time comes, the sow—she is now described as being "in farrow"—makes a fairly comfortable den in the thick brush. The young, though small at birth, are quite active; they are brown in colour, with lengthwise dark stripes and spots.

Once the offspring are old enough to travel, the groups of sows and their young (known as "sounders") join company. By the time that the acorns begin to fall in autumn, there is a general migratory movement to groves of oak trees. In Iran, at this time of the year, the hillsides are often black with teeming herds of wild boars.

Originally the Eurasian wild boar roamed over all the forested parts of Europe, east across Asia and Siberia to the Pacific coast, and south into North Africa. As with most animals that are spread over an extensive range, the wild boar varies quite a bit in appearance, depending on the localities where it flourishes.

INTERESTING WILD BOARS OF THE EAST

The Soor, Indian or Crested Wild Boar, *Sus cristatus,* is the common wild pig of India. Formidable when aroused, it has been known to kill a tiger. It stands almost three feet at the shoulder and weighs about 250 pounds. A distinct crest of long, stiff, black bristles extends from the back of the head down the neck to the shoulders.

Like its northern relative, the crested wild boar lives in the forests and builds a nest of leaves and sticks for raising its offspring.

The Babiroussa, or Celebes Pig Deer, *Babirussa babyrussa,* is not considered a true pig. However, it does belong to the hog family, and not to the deer family as one of its names implies.

A strange-looking, unlovely creature, the babiroussa is almost completely devoid of hair, and the bare grey skin is lined and heavily wrinkled. The whole animal appears to be wedge-shaped, but in reverse, tapering down evenly from the high hind quarters to the low shoulders and the snout of the pointed, relatively small head.

The most remarkable feature of the babiroussa is its weirdly shaped tusks, which run to as much as seventeen inches in length. In the upper jaw of the male these teeth, instead of projecting outwards as in most other pigs, rise straight upward, piercing the skin of the upper lip, then turn backwards in a sweeping curl; they may even reach the forehead! The lower tusks are shorter and more slender. Such fantastic tusks seem to be of little or no use to the animal and are a mere "sport" of nature.

The Celebes babiroussa is a herd animal with the habits of most wild hogs. It dwells in jungles and woodlands, preferably in places near water, since it is an excellent swimmer. This wild swine, which stands somewhat over two feet at the shoulder and weighs a bit over 125 pounds, has frequently been domesticated by native tribes.

FREAKISH TUSKS WITHOUT PURPOSE

With its curving tusks, its ugly, shovel-shaped snout, and its wrinkled, hairless grey skin, the babiroussa is far from being an appealing creature. The tusks, which may grow to seventeen inches in length, project straight up from the jaw, pierce the skin, and curve backwards, often reaching the forehead. They are apparently of no use to their owner.

Pygmy Hogs and Bearded Pigs. The Pygmy Hog, *Sus salvanius*, dwells in the forests of the Himalayas in Nepal, Sikkim, and Bhutan. The smallest of all the pigs, it weighs between ten and seventeen pounds. Small herds of about a dozen individuals frequent the tall grass of the jungles. The Bearded Pig of Borneo and Sumatra is a peculiar-looking blackish swine with short, rounded ears, extensive, curly white whiskers, and a wartlike growth covered with bristles between nose and eyes. A tall, lanky pig, it is very high at the shoulders. There are other pigs on the islands of the South Pacific.

AFRICAN WILD PIGS

The African Bush Pig or Red River Hog, *Potamochoerus porcus*, is a wary creature but fierce and tough as well. Seldom seen (it is active at night), it frequents the dense bush and heavily forested regions.

To the Boers of South Africa, this animal is known as the Boschvark (literally, "bush pig"). The bush pig's coat varies in hue from reddish brown to dark grey or black. Long, tufted ears border the face, which is marked by two pairs of gristly warts growing over bony bases— a large pair in front of the sunken, typically piggish eyes, and a smaller pair behind.

CREATURE OF THE BUSH

The red river hog, one of the South African bush pigs, is the only wild pig at home in Madagascar. Bush pigs are found in many parts of Africa south of the Sahara; they favour reeded areas or low bush country. Many have a large white stripe along the middle of the back. These big porkers avoid man, but will fight to the death if cornered.

The African bush pig dwells south of the Sahara Desert. It averages a little over two feet at the shoulder and weighs about two hundred pounds. It has a relative in Madagascar—the only member of the even-toed hoofed mammal group that is native to the island.

The Giant Forest Hog, *Hylochoerus meinertzhageni*, was discovered only as recently as 1904. Living in the deep forests, this secretive animal rarely comes out in the open, and we have been able to glean very little authentic information about its habits and life history.

We do know, however, that the giant forest hog is a "giant"—it stands thirty inches at the shoulder and weighs up to 265 pounds. It has very long, bristly hair and a broad, greatly expanded disc on the snout. The animal's range extends from Mt. Kenya west through the basin of the Congo River to the Atlantic coast.

The Wart Hog or Vlakvark, *Phacochoerus aethiopicus,* has the distinction, if you want to call it that, of usually being considered the ugliest creature on earth. Its head looks enormous in relation to its small, round, fat body, its short legs, and its small feet. With two pairs of warts on the sides of the flat scooplike face, and bleary little piggish eyes sunk in bags of wrinkled skin, the head is fantastically repulsive.

A PERFECT SCORE FOR UGLINESS

No other pig can lay claim to so many repulsive features as the wart hog of Africa. Its face is covered with warts, bumps, and gristle growths. Its eyes are deeply embedded in sacs of creased skin. Stumpy legs support its heavy grey body, and its overlarge head tapers down to a long, flat snout. The animal makes its home in a hole abandoned by an aardvark or some other creature. Hunters generally find it easy prey.

Near the end of the broad snout are the tusks, which curl out to the side, then up and over. Ten inches is about average for the tusks, though some may measure up to twenty-seven inches. Apart from the few white whiskers on the face, and the scanty mane of dark, long, coarse bristles, the animal has little hair. A large boar stands thirty inches at the shoulder and weighs two hundred pounds or more.

Active during all hours of the day, the wart hog favours the open grassy plains of central and north-eastern Africa. Though this beast, like other hogs, will dig up the ground for roots and tubers, it is occasionally seen grazing on the plains with herds of zebras and antelopes.

WHERE PIGS BELONG IN THE ANIMAL KINGDOM

We have already had a look at some of the pigs, but we have not yet considered what position they occupy in the animal kingdom. Although they have hoofs, these are not the same as the horse's or rhino's. Pigs belong to the large group of even-toed hoofed mammals. As we have seen, the term "even-toed" does not refer to the *number* of toes. These creatures have no first toe at all, and the second and fifth toes are often lacking as well. Where the second and fifth toes are present, they generally serve no major purpose.

So it is the third and fourth toes that matter, and that is why these animals are called "even-toed". On solid ground it is these toes that support the weight of the body. All the members of this order are called the Artiodactyla, a word meaning "even-fingered".

The group is in turn divided into three smaller sections, or sub-orders. These are:

The Suiformes—the ones that do not chew the cud: the pigs, peccaries, and hippopotamuses.

The Tylopoda ("knobby feet")— primitive ruminants, or cud-chewers, that have tusklike outer incisor teeth as well as canines in the upper jaw. In this group we find the camels, dromedaries, llamas, alpacas, vicuñas, and guanacos.

The Ruminantia—these are the true ruminants, that have no teeth at the front of the upper jaw. In this group are all the animals that have paired horns or antlers supported by bony outgrowths of the skull: all the deer, antelopes, sheep, goats, cattle, and giraffes.

Of course it is not because they have horns or antlers that we call these animals ruminants. That word simply means that the creature to which we apply it chews the cud. The stomach, instead of being a simple compartment, is divided into a series of three—sometimes four —chambers. The first one is called the rumen (whence the group name). A ruminant has the advantage over other kinds of animals of being able to swallow large quantities of food quickly and store it up in the rumen. At leisure, the ruminant brings the food back up into its mouth and chews it thoroughly so it can be digested easily.

It is interesting to observe how a ruminant chews its cud—the undigested food brought up from the stomach. As the animal chews, the lower jaw moves from side to side, but only the teeth at one side of the jaw are in contact at one time. After a brief period, the cud is shifted over to the other cheek and milled on that side for a while.

With these distinctions in mind, we may turn back to the pigs and their interesting relatives and understand them better, now that we understand their place in nature.

PECCARIES—PIGLIKE CREATURES OF THE NEW WORLD

Peccaries are forest animals and travel in bands ranging from a few individuals to as many as three hundred. Like the true pigs, they are rooters, feeding on tubers, roots, fruits, and other vegetable matter. But they also prey on small animal life, including snakes.

A peccary never misses a chance to kill even a large rattlesnake. With its mane and body hair bristling in all directions, the peccary fiercely charges to within three feet of the reptile, stops short, and feints it into striking. As the snake lies uncoiled for an instant, the peccary suddenly leaps into the air; with its back arched and its feet together, it comes slashing down on all four hoofs. Again and again it does this, until it has cut the snake to ribbons. (The domestic pig, it should be noted, is also an efficient destroyer of snakes, including rattlers.)

We sometimes read tales of ferocious bands of peccaries attacking human beings. This makes interesting reading but has little foundation in fact. The truth of the matter seems to be that, in general, the peccary is a shy and retiring creature, fighting only for self-protection.

PECCARIES AND PIGS

Peccaries are the only piglike animals native to America, but they are not true pigs. The most obvious differences that separate the peccaries from the Old World pigs include: the loss of the small outer hoof on the hind foot; straight tusks that point downward, in the upper jaw; a large musk gland on the back, about eight inches above the tail.

The peccary's tanned hide, especially durable and popular as glove leather, can be recognized by the pattern of evenly distributed groups of three holes left by hair-roots.

Both peccaries and Old World pigs behave in much the same way, though there is a slight difference in breeding habits. The den may be a hollow tree, or a nest in a thicket. At birth the young are about the size of a rabbit, and yellowish brown in colour with a black stripe down the back. Two babies are normal for a litter; occasionally there is only one, and in rare cases there are three.

Pigs make up the family Suidae. The peccaries have their own family, Tayassuidae.

There are two kinds of peccaries, divided into smaller groups that differ a bit in size and markings, as well as the regions they live in. We find them all the way from southern Texas and Arizona down to Patagonia.

The Collared Peccary, Javeline, or Musk Hog, *Tagassu tajacu,* dwells in the extreme southern United States and south to Patagonia— sometimes at sea-level, sometimes at altitudes of eight thousand feet. A

ONE OF AMERICA'S NATIVE "PIGS"

The peccaries, animals of the Western Hemisphere, are not true pigs, though they closely resemble them. They are furious fighters when attacked, and are fully capable of smashing a large rattlesnake to bits. Legend has it that they will attack human beings, but this has never been proved; confronted by man, the peccary would rather retire, and only fights to save its own skin. Above is the collared peccary, a native of southern North America as well as of South America.

light-coloured stripe almost encircles the body at the shoulders to form a collar.

This animal is covered with thick, coarse, bristlelike hair, grizzled in colour; it does not have much of a tail. About twenty inches high at the shoulder, the collared peccary is three feet long and weighs about fifty pounds.

The White-lipped Peccary. *Tagassu pecari*, is larger than its collared cousin and lacks the shoulder stripes. Its coarse black hair is relieved by a white area that reaches from the chin nearly to the eye. This animal is not quite so far-ranging as the collared variety, living in the region that extends from southern Mexico to Paraguay. In South America the white-lipped peccary prefers low country.

HIPPOPOTAMUSES—RIVER-HORSES OF AFRICA

"Hippopotamus" comes from the Greek and literally means "river-horse". It is a large, ungainly word, very suitable for this large, ungainly creature. The hippo, as we may conveniently call it, has a bulky, rotund body, and legs so short that its ample belly barely misses scraping the ground. Its enormous head rounds out into a bulbous snout.

The hippo's nostrils and eyes are located quite strategically. The nostrils are placed forward and on top of the snout, while the small, bulging eyes are high up on the front of the head. When the animal is swimming, it can breathe and see while only the very top of its flat face is exposed above the water-line. The ears, by the way, are small and rounded, set well back on the head behind the eyes.

In prehistoric times the hippo lived in Europe. In those far-off days, it was common in the valley of the Thames and ranged north to Yorkshire as a contemporary of primitive man. Eventually the hippos disappeared everywhere but in Africa, and they are now making their last stand on the Dark Continent.

The family name of the hippos is big, the content small. The Hippopotamidae family contains just the Common Hippo and the Pygmy Hippo.

THE COMMON HIPPOPOTAMUS—INTERESTING,
BUT NO BEAUTY

The Common Hippopotamus, *Hippopotamus amphibius*, once frequented most of the large lakes and rivers of Africa, but today we do not find it south of Zululand. It lives unmolested in crocodile-infested waters, too formidable an adversary for even these powerful reptiles. Its canines can rip through the crocodile's armour plate with one bite.

The hippo does not mind salt or brackish water. Not a fast or particularly adept swimmer, it is built for slow paddling and walking on the bottom in shallow water as it roots up water plants with its tusks. However, it swims powerfully enough to be able to make its way upstream against a strong current.

Though it feeds chiefly on the reeds and grasses that abound in and around watery surroundings, the hippo comes ashore under cover of darkness to raid the market gardens of the people. Hippos frequently bask in the sunshine on the lakes and rivers of Africa, each animal pillowing its head on another's back. How restful this may be is not clear, for some say that a full-grown hippo's head weighs a ton!

The hippo has an adjusting mechanism for the time it spends in the dry atmosphere, when it has come ashore to feed; it is equipped with special skin pores that secrete a thick, oily, pinkish substance. This secretion may also act as a protective measure against extended periods in the water. The process of giving off the pinkish fluid from the skin gave rise to the illusion that the hippo "sweats blood".

The hippo can float like a log or sink like ballast and run along the bottom of a lake at eight miles an hour. It generally submerges for about two minutes at a time, but it can stay under water for as long as thirty minutes if necessary. The valvelike nostrils close when the animal dives; as it surfaces, they open with a loud snort and a fine, moist spray is expelled a foot high. When a hippo sports at night, its blowings and snortings can be heard at a considerable distance. During the daytime the animal sleeps on a sandy bank or among thick beds of reeds.

IT MAY WEIGH FOUR TONS

The hippo will never win a bathing beauty contest, yet it is a most interesting animal to look at closely. Its size is most impressive. A hippo will weigh up to four tons, and stand four and one-half feet at the shoulder. Its head-and-body length may come to twelve feet, and the tail is another foot long. Except for a few bristly hairs on the nose, head, and tail, the animal is naked. Its skin is thick and dark brownish in colour.

Next to the whale, the hippo has the largest mouth of any mammal. We get the impression that this beast takes great delight in displaying the awesome gape of its tremendous jaws.

The hippo's incisor and canine teeth are large, with sharp edges that are kept honed as the teeth of the upper and lower jaw grind past each other when the mouth opens and closes. The lower canines may reach four to seven pounds in weight and over twenty-four inches in length. More than half of this huge expanse, though, is hidden beneath the gum line. These sickle-shaped teeth are well suited for cutting the tall reeds, grasses, and water plants on which the hippo feeds. The tusks are commercially valuable as a source of ivory. (However, the ivory they yield is very brittle, and splinters with the expansion and contraction produced by heat and cold.)

By now you may have gathered that the author has something of a special admiration for hippos. As a rule, he finds it hard to forgo an opportunity to photograph them. Some years ago, while he was taking a picture of a bull hippo swimming near the edge of a lagoon in East Africa, one of his companions fired a big elephant gun at the creature. At the time the members of the party were apparently standing on floating masses of vegetation. With the force of the shock of the gun's discharge, the vegetation tipped and the men lost their footing. Meanwhile the hippo sank.

Next morning the body of the animal was seen floating, and natives from far and near had congregated on the bank in anticipation of a feast. However, their fear of crocodiles kept them out of the water. After much argument, they seized one screaming member of their motley crew and hurled him bodily through the air to the farther side of the floating body. Discovering in this way that no snapping jaws of crocodiles were in evidence, they all waded in and dragged the great beast on to the beach. It was not long before all the meat had been stripped from the bones and carried away to the village.

The meat of the hippo is rather stringy and has a machine-oil taste. Yet the natives love it, especially the fat, which they render down as lard. They claim that it never goes rancid.

HIPPOS' TRAVELS AND TASTES

A hippo is more active than is generally supposed. It can run on land as fast as a man, and even gallop at a considerable speed. When running or walking, its legs are so widely separated on either side of its fat body that two parallel lines of tracks are left on the sand or mud.

Old bulls usually live alone, but twenty or thirty individuals may keep together and cover long distances in search of food, often travelling twenty or twenty-five miles by river in one night. Usually, however, they will not venture more than a mile or so, in order to be able to get back to their sleeping quarters before daylight.

BIG COUSIN OF THE PIGS

The hippo's flat, grotesque face is admirably constructed for the life this animal leads in Africa's rivers. The tiny eyes are placed high and close together; the nostrils are well forward, on top of the snout. When the hippo journeys in the water, the top of its face remains above the surface, and so the great beast is able to breathe and see while swimming. This four-ton creature is very much a vegetarian.

The famous wandering hippo Huberta created world-wide interest by travelling some 1,200 miles. Leaving Zululand in November, 1928, Huberta arrived at the Keiskama River in April, 1931; there, unfortunately, the beast was shot. Huberta had an uncanny habit of showing up unexpectedly and then stealing away silently into the bush, or disappearing quietly into the water before anyone could come close.

If hippos wander too far from water, they expose themselves to attack by lions. On one occasion, three of the big cats jumped at a hippo and the deafening roar of the conflict could be heard at a camp a mile away. Dragging its assailants with it, the hippo managed to struggle along until it reached the water and escaped.

Hippos apparently object to campfires. Generally they voice their resentment with loud grunts, but, on occasion, they have been known to go further, climbing on to shore and charging the offending fire, to the consternation of the campers. Aside from such grunts, Mr. Hippo's vocal achievements consist of low, panting breaths followed by trumpeting snorts that end in a roaring bellow of considerable and somewhat frightening volume.

BABY HIPPOS

Hippos are sociable beasts, gathering in herds of twenty to thirty. When mating time arrives, the bulls turn savage, and fight brutal battles among themselves for possession of the females. Often these duels end fatally as the fighters cut huge three-inch gashes in each other's hide with their sharp tusks.

Hippos mate once a year. Eight or nine months later, the female comes ashore or retreats to a bed of reeds to give birth to her single calf. The baby hippo weighs about one hundred pounds at birth and can swim before it can walk. Suckling usually takes place in the water. During the period of infancy the young rides its mother's back in the water.

A baby hippo must stand up to nurse, whether in shallow water or on land. Park keepers experience great difficulty in getting newborn hippos to suckle. It is not always possible to duplicate natural conditions, where the baby calf can be in the water yet at the same time be able to stand on the bottom and hold its mouth high enough out of the water to reach its mother's udder.

A HIPPO NAMED PETE

A large bull hippo named Pete was born in 1903 and died in 1953 a few months short of the half-century mark. By the time he was three years old, he weighed 1,700 pounds. When he grew up he weighed about two tons, as estimated by his water displacement. His daily rations were ninety pounds of hay and thirty-six pounds of soup. He spent most of his life in jovial acceptance of his lot at the Bronx Park Zoo in New York, finally dying of old age. A bull hippo at the London Zoo weighed 8,960 pounds—probably a record.

TALL TALE?

Native African tradition tells of a huge, strange animal, known as a chipekwe, that lives in the waters of fifty-mile-long Lake Bangweulu. Described as having a smooth body like a hippopotamus, this creature is supposed to be armed with a horn like a rhinoceros. The horn is said to be of white ivory, smooth and highly polished.

No such animal has come out of Africa, but then, in recent years, many of the so-called mysterious beasts that were known only to the natives have turned up as actually existing in remote parts of Africa. Perhaps Mr. Chipekwe will prove to be real after all.

PYGMY HIPPOS

The Pygmy Hippopotamus, *Choeropsis liberiensis*, frequents small rivers in deep forest country in Liberia and Sierra Leone in West Africa. It spends much of its time on land and sleeps during the day in a den under a river bank. A little under three feet at the shoulder and six feet long, this animal weighs a mere four hundred pounds— truly a pygmy among the hippos.

In general, except for being smaller and less sociable, the life, habits, and appearance of the pygmy hippo are quite similar to those of its huge relative. Even its life span in the wild state—thirty to thirty-five years—is the same; and the female gives birth to her baby after the same interval after mating.

Camels and Llamas—
Beasts of Burden Since Ancient Days

CAMELS, on first acquaintance, appear to be supercilious creatures with smug, disdainful expressions. Even worse—they may strike us as bad tempered, irritable, and obstinate. Seemingly placid and stupid, they are keen enough to resent actively any form of ill-treatment. With tenacious memory, camels will carry a grudge for a long time, waiting for the opportunity to get even when the offender is off guard. These beasts show their displeasure in a most unsavoury manner: they turn the head to spit contemptuously full in the face of the person they resent.

Their relatives the llamas are equally quick to show their annoyance. If they are loaded too heavily, they grumble in their guttural voices and often lie down and refuse to budge. They also spit at the offending driver—with a remarkable degree of accuracy. The charge consists of a disgusting green mess of half-digested grass that is exploded violently through the mouth and nose.

But these qualities are only part—a very minor part—of the story of these animals and their immense usefulness to man over a period of thousands of years.

The scientists tell us, surprisingly enough, that the camel family had its start, not in Asia as we might suppose, but in North America. That was about forty million years ago. By the end of the Pleistocene epoch, barely a million years ago, the camel family had spread to South America—and to Asia as well, by an intercontinental land bridge that existed in prehistoric times.

What about the camel family today? The camels and llamas make up a fast-waning group that has almost disappeared in the wild state. Only two truly wild varieties are left. Both belong to the llamas, the New World branch of the family. Restricted to South America, the llamas frequent upland plains and, more generally, the highlands of

BIG, WATER-LOVING COUSINS OF THE PIGS

The hippopotamus, a relative of the pig, is common along many of the waterways of tropical Africa, where it has been known to overturn small boats. If undisturbed, however, it is a peaceful animal; it is quite sociable by nature and is often seen in large herds. At night the hippo frequently wanders several miles across country in search of food. See page 692.

Arabian American Oil Company

CAMELS DRINKING AT AN OASIS TROUGH IN SAUDI ARABIA
The Arabian camels pictured here are taller, faster animals than their cousins the Bactrian camels, and have only one hump. Camels are particularly well adapted for life in the desert: they have special cavities in the stomach which store water, the fatty hump serves as a food reserve, and the feet are broad and cushioned, which makes walking across the sands easier.
See page 698.

the Andes. The camels, of course, are creatures of the Asiatic and African deserts.

The camel family (Camelidae) makes up the suborder Tylopoda, as we have seen—one of the groups in the order of even-toed hoofed mammals.

HOW CAMELS ARE ADAPTED FOR LIFE IN THE DESERT

Camels are very hardy and can bear up under extreme privation. These are ideal qualities in a beast of burden that is used in regions ranging from broiling arid deserts to freezing mountain country.

The camel's body is covered with soft, fine, woolly hair, usually dark brown or yellowish brown in colour, from which high-quality cloth is made. The flesh and milk are food and drink to some native peoples. The hump of the camel is composed of fatty tissue used by the animal as a reserve of sustenance when the food supply runs low.

As for the stomach, it has three chambers. One of them is lined with water-storing cells that can hold upwards of a gallon. A camel can go three days without drinking and suffer little inconvenience. One camel has been observed to go thirty-four days without drinking; this, however, is far above the usual capacity for doing without water. Given free access to water, a camel will consume from five to seven gallons each day.

Camels are vegetarians and cud-chewers. Unlike the typical ruminants that keep the food on one side of the mouth for some time, the camel constantly works the cud from side to side with each champ of the jaws. The tusklike outer incisor teeth and canines of the upper jaws, excellent for cutting herbage, can also inflict a severe and painful bite.

The creature's ears are small and inconspicuous. Well-haired, slit-like nostrils can be closed against windblown sand, while a double row of heavy lashes protects the eyes from particles of flying grit. Long legs and broad feet are further adaptations for life on the shifting sandy wastes. The foot is made up of two toes provided with thick, cushioned soles and nail-like hoofs. Camels walk with a long, swinging stride. They pace—that is, the front and rear legs on the same side of the body move forward in unison. This produces a rolling effect that may have some connection with the animal's being called the "ship of the desert".

EAL / 6—F

THE MATING OF CAMELS

There are several misleading and even fantastic beliefs about the mating habits of the camel. Strangely enough, some of these notions are given credence in recently published literature and in what would seem reliable sources.

It has been said, for example, that the reason there are no wild camels today is that they require human assistance when they breed. Since this was not sufficiently available in the past, or so the theory goes, only domestic camels can survive.

A careful survey of the facts reveals no backing for such an idea. There is nothing unusual about the mating of the camel, except that the male or stallion puts his head over the back of his mate and forces her to sit down, with her feet folded beneath her. The procedure from here on is the same as in other four-footed beasts of the field. During mating, the herd surrounds the pair, giving them privacy in the open desert wastes.

Camels do not have a fixed breeding season; they mate throughout the year. The baby camel is born 315 to 389 days after mating has taken place.

Throughout Asia and Africa we find two distinct species, the Bactrian and Dromedary Camels; the regions where they live overlap to a certain extent. From time to time, camels have been introduced with varying success in southern Europe, Australia, and even the United States.

BACTRIAN AND DROMEDARY CAMELS

The Bactrian Camel, or Mecheri, *Camelus bactrianus*, is the two-humped camel common through central Asia from China to Turkistan. The average caravan of these pack animals travels at a rate of two to three miles per hour and thirty miles per day; each camel bears a load of about four hundred pounds.

Though not so slender, handsome, or speedy as the African variety, the Bactrian camel is stronger and more heavily built. Measuring seven feet to the top of the hump, it has stout, moderately long limbs. The body hair is longer and shaggier than on the dromedary; this makes it possible for the Bactrian camel to withstand the rigours of the colder climate prevailing in its range.

The Dromedary, or Heirie, *Camelus dromedarius*, is the one-humped camel of the hot, arid Arabian deserts. Slimmer and sleeker-looking than the Bactrian type, it is a riding camel, with longer legs, better suited for swift travel than for carrying great burdens.

THE DROMEDARY CAMEL AND THE PYRAMIDS ARE OLD FRIENDS

We no longer find the dromedary or one-humped camel of Egypt and Arabia in the wild —this fine desert mount was tamed long ago, and exists today only as a servant of man. Its cousin, the Bactrian or two-humped camel, may still be encountered enjoying its freedom in the Gobi Desert, but doubtless it is the descendant of escaped domestic animals. Camels have a savage temper when aroused, and have been known to kill men.

A dromedary will keep up a pace of eight to ten miles per hour for eighteen hours—one specimen has been known to cover 115 miles in eleven hours over the deserts of Egypt. The soles of the feet are softer and more tender than those of the Bactrian camel—hence the dromedary is less suited to hard and rocky terrain.

CAMEL CARAVANS

To the Arab, the camel is an absolute necessity. It provides him with transportation, of course—and also with milk, meat, and clothing.

True, he prides himself on his horses, but they are for show. No horse could keep up with a camel caravan travelling three or four miles an hour for eight or ten hours a day.

The Arabs drive the camel herds to pasture for a month on waterless plains; at this time the herdsmen survive on the camels' milk. Large camels are expected to carry loads of from four hundred to six hundred pounds, and to travel twenty-five or thirty miles per day.

The author has often seen the Kirghiz women milking camels early in the morning. The animals are so tall that the women stand up to milk them. The milk is then fermented into *kumiss*, a pleasing beverage which these people drink regularly during the warm summer weather.

Despite the camel's evil reputation, the author personally has great admiration for the animal. A caravan of camels with their robed drivers crossing the burning deserts of Asia is one of the most impressive sights he has ever seen. Camels are stoical, hardy individuals that move steadily along at one uniform pace, never hurrying or lagging from daybreak until far into the dark.

Camels obey orders like good soldiers, though often with grunts of protest when being loaded. Occasionally one will go on a rampage. The author recalls an occasion when one of his camels in central Asia started to buck; its long legs seemed to be flying in all directions while cooking utensils and personal equipment were spread all over the landscape. It was some time before the drivers could stop laughing long enough to catch the beast. One young camel that was being weaned kept up such a constant bleat all night long that it was hard to get a chance to sleep.

The fact remains that when raised and treated with kindness and understanding, a camel is just as co-operative and helpful as a horse.

CAMELS IN ANCIENT TIMES

Camels are descendants of a stock that has been in man's service for at least five thousand years, or since the beginning of recorded history. These animals were known in ancient China. The Babylonians were using camels about 1,000 B.C.

From the Old Testament we learn that Abraham had sheep, oxen, asses, and camels. Job, when he was a rich man, had three thousand camels, and later doubled that number. In Abraham's day, camels were needed not only for milk, but as beasts of burden when travelling over the wild, pathless land. The life of Abraham must have been much like that of the Bedouin chieftain of today.

Thousands of years after Abraham, the famous phrase about the camel and the needle's eye turns up in the New Testament. In Oriental towns there are small gates called "needle's eyes". These are used by late travellers who wish to enter the town after the main gates have been closed. The openings are too low for a camel to pass through in the ordinary way. The beast kneels down and, after having been unloaded, is able to shuffle through on its knees.

CAMELS IN THE UNITED STATES

Few Americans are aware that these odd-looking creatures came close to being established as accredited domesticated animals in the United States. The attempt began in 1855, when Congress appropriated thirty thousand dollars to introduce camels for use in the frontier garrisons and settlements of the Southwest, where Indians were particularly troublesome.

On 15 February, 1856, the ship *Supply* sailed from Smyrna carrying a cargo of thirty-three camels. Other shipments were also made, and a number of private firms followed the government's example. However, the camels did not prove a success and most of them were turned loose. Soon they became a menace to crops and stampeded horses. Nevada passed an act prohibiting camels at large anywhere within its borders. The camels, now running wild, were shot on sight.

The last of the marauders met its death in Yuma, Arizona, in 1899 and was eaten by the Indians. A newspaper commented: "The venerable beast was one of the herd of camels brought from Asia Minor years ago to carry ore from Comstock Mines. So ends the greatest attempt at acclimating foreign animals ever made in the United States."

LLAMAS OF THE PLAINS AND MOUNTAIN SLOPES

Whereas the Old World camel is a creature of the desert, its New World relative the llama dwells on grassy plains and mountain slopes. There are four kinds of llamas; two are domestic, while the other two may still be found in the wild state. These South American cud-chewers are slender and more lightly built than camels; they have long, pointed ears, a short bushy tail, and generally a thick woolly coat. The feet, like those of the true camels, are two-toed and padded on the soles. The back is not humped. The animals pace like the camels.

LLAMAS—THE INCA'S BEST SERVANTS

The Llama, *Lama glama*, was life to the Inca; its meat fed him, its wool kept him warm, its hide covered his feet, its fat was made into candles and gave him light. Its hair was twisted into ropes, and even its droppings were not wasted—they were dried and used for fuel to warm his body. The llama carried the Inca's burdens even up in the thin air at seventeen thousand feet. (Only the male, by the way, was used as a pack animal; it started to work at the age of three years.)

Knowing what a treasure they had in the llama, the Incas took very good care of the animal. They never harnessed it to a plough or a cart. They do not seem to have taken milk from the llama, probably because the supply was too scanty; there was just barely enough to feed the one baby llama that was born in February or March when the snow still drifted in the highlands of Peru.

Farmers packed the animal with small loads. They used its wool for textiles but never beat it into felt. They ate its meat, but never as a regular part of their diet. The Incas sliced the llama's flesh into thin strips and dried it in the sun. The Peruvian name for this emergency ration is *charqui*, a word that seems to have been corrupted by English-speaking people into "jerky".

Holding the llama in high esteem as they did, the Incas considered it as their most valuable sacrifice for religious festivals. They always used the male for this purpose; it was forbidden to kill females. To each Inca god, a special kind of llama was dedicated. Thus to Viracocha, the all-highest god of the Incas, a brown llama was sacrificed. White llamas, symbolic of royal authority, were destined for the Sun God. Animals of mixed colours (signifying clouds) were offered to the Thunder God.

The domestication of this relative of the camel was limited to the Peruvian empire, where it was developed, unprompted by any outside influence. By the time the Spaniards arrived in Peru in the sixteenth century, the Incas had been using the llama for well over two thousand years. To the conquering Spaniards, the animal was the "Peruvian sheep".

Llamas Today. The llama is the strongest and largest of the four species of South American camel-like cud-chewers; a full-grown male measures about four feet at the shoulder. The hair varies in colour from brown, or almost black, to white. Head, neck, and limbs are covered with short hair, while the body proper is blanketed in longer hair, dense but soft and fine to the touch.

The strength, size, sure-footedness, and comparative abundance of the llama make it an excellent beast of burden today as yesterday. It is particularly valuable in rough mining country, where it has been used to transport ores from the mountains to the waterways and sea-coast. The animals can cover twelve to fifteen miles a day on this difficult terrain. Depending on their size, llamas carry a load of from sixty-five to two hundred pounds.

The load is placed in saddle bags of woven llama hair, fastened with a rawhide llama rope. If it feels overloaded, this strong-willed beast immediately sits down and refuses to move, even when severely cudgelled. As we have seen, it will resort to spitting if goaded too far. Only the males are used as beasts of burden, the females being reserved for breeding purposes.

THE LLAMA'S RELATIVES

The Alpaca, *Lama pacos*, is smaller than the llama proper, and more sheeplike in appearance. Its fleece may reach a length of two feet, barely clearing the ground. The springy yet silky fibres are woven into a strong durable cloth that is famous the world over. Both the llama and alpaca are domesticated types that are supposed to have originated from the guanaco. However, it may be that the alpaca is the descendant of a third breed that is now extinct.

The Guanaco or Huanaco, *Lama guanicoe*, ranges in herds of up to and over a hundred throughout the pampas of Argentina and Patagonia as well as in the mountains of Peru, Bolivia, and Chile. A good swimmer, it has been seen crossing from island to island in the Cape Horn region. In Patagonia there are great accumulations of bones, which may indicate either a natural communal graveyard or mass slaughter by the natives or early Spaniards.

The guanaco stands about three and one-half feet at the highest point of the back. To many observers, this animal seems to be more like a hornless goat antelope than a camel in superficial appearance. Its flesh is greatly relished by the Indian tribes in the vicinity of its range.

Up to a few years ago, the camel family was the only branch of the mammals that had been left untouched by the fur trade. (True, the wool of the alpaca, vicuña, and camel has been used from time immemorial for making fine cloth.) Originally a wild animal, the guanaco is now raised extensively on farms for its wool and also for its pelt, which is used by the fur trade for making short fur coats and for trimmings.

SOUTH AMERICAN KINSMAN OF THE CAMEL

A close look at the guanaco, one of the llamas, may not reveal its relationship to the camel, but the animals are kinsmen all the same. The guanaco is a smaller animal, of course, and it is not so sturdily built; it also lacks a hump. Although it does not have the strength of the camel, the guanaco is important as a beast of burden in South America.

The guanaco's soft woolly hair is pale yellowish brown on the body, while the head is ashy grey. The newborn young are killed to obtain skins for the beautiful robes called *capas*. The pelt is sold under the name *Guanaquito*. Used in its natural colour or dyed deep brown, it has a general resemblance to fox fur.

Guanacos mate in August or September, and the baby is born ten or eleven months later. The mother nurses the young for six weeks, weans it for another six, and after that the youngster is on its own. There is only a single young at birth.

The Vicuña, or Vicugna, *Vicugna vicugna*, was prized so highly by the Incas that they prescribed the death penalty for anyone who molested this beast without direct authority from the state. The fabric (known as *cumpi*) made from vicuña hair was reserved for Inca royalty. Human hair has been likened to a piece of wire as compared to a silky strand of vicuña wool. Thus, among the hoofed mammals, the animal has the same position as the chinchilla among the rodents.

A domesticated beast, the vicuña still lives in the wild state as well. Standing less than three feet at the shoulder, it is tawny in colour with a white bib on the brisket; unlike most members of the llama group, it does not have an excessively luxuriant coat.

Dwelling at skyscraping altitudes on the slopes of the Andes, the vicuña ranges over Ecuador, Peru, Bolivia, and Chile. This animal travels in small herds of six to twelve females and their young, headed by a lone male. The herd leader, it seems, keeps watch from the highest point in the vicinity of the band. At the approach of danger, he utters a shrill whistle and covers the rear of the retreating herd.

Chevrotains—
Mouse Deer of the Jungles

CHEVROTAINS, though they have no horns, look like diminutive, delicately fashioned deer. Silently they tiptoe about with a stilted gait that makes you think their long slender legs are stiff-kneed and have no joints.

Actually, these creatures of the tropical jungles of Asia and Africa resemble camels and pigs in some respects, deer in others. They are the smallest of all the Asiatic hoofed mammals, approaching the hare in size. The males have tusklike upper canine teeth that project below the mouth like those of certain wild swine.

The chevrotains, or "mouse deer", as they are popularly known, are neither mice nor deer. They are sufficiently distinctive to justify their being placed in a family all by themselves—Tragulidae ("little he-goats").

TINIEST HOOFED MAMMAL IN ASIA

Only the size of a hare, the chevrotain is a delicate animal with long, protruding upper canines that grow down below its mouth. Though zoologically incorrect, its other name, "mouse deer", certainly describes its slender, deerlike body. Quietly the chevrotain walks about the jungle, its thin legs held so stiffly they seem to have no joints at all.

Rather abundant in the regions they frequent, chevrotains are shy and wary, as you would expect of vegetarian animals that lack great strength, impenetrable hides, sharp claws, horns, or other effective means of defence. And their jungle enemies are numerous—snakes, lizards, and flesh-eating mammals.

The little chevrotain is a fair climber, frequently taking refuge in the lower branches of trees when attacked. Some say that when the chevrotain is pursued by hounds, it will jump up in the bushes and hang itself from a branch by its hooked canine teeth until the danger is over. However, the author is not inclined to believe that this is true.

This little creature may make its home four or five thousand feet up in the mountains, but it is most common in low country. It lies up during the heat of the day, preferably in crevices among rocks and other sheltered places; it ventures out to feed only at dusk.

The chevrotain is often found frequenting jungle paths and along roadsides at night. Taken young, it is easily tamed and will not run off into the bush. It has been known to breed in captivity. The only sound it utters is a feeble bleat.

June and July are the months for the rutting season, when the males remain with the females; at all other times both sexes—except

ITS ONLY DEFENCE IS TO HIDE

To fight its many enemies, the timid chevrotain has not the strength, sharp horns, claws, or any of the other means of protection animals generally have. It can only withdraw into the bush or up trees. The water chevrotain, above, stays in the African marshes, where it rarely ventures out of the tall reeds, so that it is seldom seen by man. An olive-brown coat, streaked with white, blends with its surroundings and helps in concealment.

females with young—are solitary. Usually two offspring result from mating.

The Spotted Chevrotain, or Indian Chevrotain, *Tragulus* (*Moschiola*) *memina*, dwells in the forests of Ceylon and southern India north to the east-central areas. This little beast is no more than a foot high at the shoulder, and its head-and-body length is twenty inches at most; it weighs about five or six pounds, and its tail is a mere stub of less than two inches. Its general body colour is light brown, with longish white or buff spots that merge in lengthwise bands along the sides.

There are also two Malayan types that are slightly larger than the Indian chevrotain; they are unspotted, with white under-parts, chin, and throat. The African Water Chevrotain, *Hyemoschus*, is somewhat larger than the Asiatic species. It frequents the lakes and water courses of the Cameroons and the Congo. Being a good swimmer, it will take to water on the least provocation.

Deer—
Antlered Creatures of the Wildwood

ALTHOUGH the deer are mostly animals of the wild, they have always been of the greatest importance to mankind. Their flesh, known as venison, may be a delicacy to us of the West, but to people in far-off places it means life itself. The deer's hide may serve many purposes, and its handsome antlers can be made into useful tools.

We find the deer in all sorts of regions. They are at home in lowland swamps, grassy plains, and sparsely covered brush country; they dwell in dense woodland, too, in mountainous terrain, and even in the snowbound wastes of the Arctic. Just as they live in many different places, so they are of many sizes—they range in bulk all the way from the dimensions of a spaniel to those of a large horse. In bygone days they were even bigger: the great Irish elk, which we know only from its remains, had antlers that stretched eleven feet from tip to tip.

EATING HABITS—BENEFICIAL OR HARMFUL?

Many deer are forest or woodland animals that feed on grass and tender bark, twigs, and shoots of trees. Thus they aid in keeping the forest floor clear of excessive underbrush. Some observers claim that by pruning the lower branches of young trees, deer aid in producing tall fine timber.

In certain regions of the United States, deer have become over-abundant. In such areas, the feeding habits of the animals are a serious menace to the woodlands as well as to farms, which the hungry creatures invade in their search for food. They spill out of the forests in all directions, and have even been known to overrun an airport, interfering with the going and coming of planes. In earlier days, when more flesh-eating animals existed, the numbers of the deer had their natural check. Today it is up to man to restore the balance.

ANTLERS—THE DEER'S CROWNING GLORY

One of the most remarkable features in the entire animal kingdom is the deer's antlers. Generally it is only the male that has them. A few species, the musk deer and the Chinese river deer for example, lack antlers in both sexes; both male and female caribou possess them.

The antlers are solid bony growths that develop from permanent bases on the frontal bones of the skull. The deer sheds them annually, usually in midwinter or early spring. About two weeks after the old antlers are dropped, a round furlike ball begins to rise from each base. Very rapidly these small growths swell and expand into the curving and branching structures that will soon grace the head. In this growing stage, the antlers are soft and spongy; their tissues are richly provided with circulating blood.

Growth continues until the supply of blood and nourishment slows down; finally it stops altogether as the blood vessels shrink and cease to function. The antlers now harden to bonelike consistency, while the overlying "velvet" dries up and peels off. The animals burnish and polish the antlers by rubbing them against tree trunks and branches

—a process doubtless prompted by the itching sensation caused by the drying up of living tissues.

This periodic loss and replacement is truly amazing; even the enormous antlers of the moose, which may weigh up to sixty pounds, fall off and reappear every year!

While antlers vary quite a bit in size and shape, those of each species of deer have their typical pattern. Often magnificent as a headdress, the antlers are also formidable as weapons. Although they may be employed against other kinds of animals, more generally the male deer uses them in battle for possession of the females.

In their courtship struggles, the males rush at each other with battering, headlong charges. However, the rivals are seldom fatally injured, as the tines, or points, form a basketwork guard that rules out most of the danger from direct piercing thrusts. Occasionally the antlers of two combatants become so firmly interlocked that the animals exhaust themselves in fruitless efforts to escape; in the end they starve to death.

Apart from their remarkable antlers, nearly all the deer are noteworthy for another reason—they lack a gall bladder. Whether this deficiency is fortunate or not, we cannot say; we know nothing about gall-bladder disease among wild animals, though it is a serious ailment in human beings. Still another peculiarity of deer is that they have no central incisors in the upper jaw, their place being taken by a pad of hard gum tissue; this is typical in ruminants. Sharp, dagger-like upper canines are usually present in deer that lack antlers.

Deer, we have seen, are ruminants. When a deer browses, fresh food is partly masticated, then swallowed, and passed on to the lobe of the stomach known as the "paunch" (rumen). Here it remains to soften and soak. At its leisure, the animal can contract this paunch and return some of the food—now called the cud—to its mouth. This time the cud is thoroughly chewed and swallowed again. Bypassing the paunch, it is digested in other parts of the stomach.

THE DEER FAMILY

There are close to a hundred forms of deer. Probably many more remain to be discovered and identified in the more remote and as yet incompletely explored wildernesses of the world.

The deer family is known as the Cervidae. These even-toed ruminants are spread throughout the Northern Hemisphere, over Asia, Europe, and North America. In the southern half of the globe, their range is limited almost entirely to South America. With the exception of certain kinds of red deer that are found in the Barbary Coast area, this family is absent from Africa, and no native species exists in Madagascar or Australia.

A DEER THE SIZE OF A DOG

Accustomed as we are to thinking of deer as fairly large animals, the Chilean pudu, smallest of American deer, seems surprisingly tiny to us. But the deer family is enormously diversified: it ranges from the massive moose, which is six feet tall and weighs fourteen hundred pounds, to the pudu, which weighs up to twenty-four pounds and stands only thirteen and one-half inches at the shoulder. Its horns are the simplest spikes.

DEER WITHOUT ANTLERS

The Musk Deer, *Moschus moschiferus*, the most primitive of the living deer, is a small creature that favours the wooded slopes at high altitudes in central Asia and at lower elevations in Siberia. We find it throughout the Himalayas as far west as Tibet and north into northern Siberia.

Usually a solitary animal, the musk deer sleeps during the day in a "form" like the hare. In the deep snows of eastern Siberia the author has seen this deer's runways and the forms where it slept. Though he often found its bed still warm, he never succeeded in glimpsing the animal before it stole silently away. The deer moves about to feed only from evening to early morning. A typical ruminant, it is a vegetarian, browsing on lichens, grasses, and foliage.

——MUSK FOR MATING. The musk which gives this deer its name is developed in an abdominal gland during the rutting season. A single animal produces about one ounce of musk. Many of these deer are killed for the "musk pod", which has considerable commercial value.

The musk is used by the Chinese to make perfume. Only males over three years old are of any value. In North China, where the musk deer is plentiful and the musk pods bring a substantial annual income to the people, the hunters are careful to kill only the grown males. This much-persecuted little deer often escapes its captors by climbing leaning trees and taking refuge in the thick tops.

The rutting season comes in January, and a single young is born in June; twins are rare. The fawns are ready to mate before they are a year old.

We have already described this animal as primitive. It has a gall bladder, but lacks antlers. Its large ears, short tail, and thick, woolly coat emphasize its resemblance to a large hare. The upper canine teeth in the male are especially long, frequently measuring two or three inches in length. The fur is lengthy, coarse, and brittle.

The musk deer is a pleasing animal to behold. Its coat is a rich dark brown, mottled or spotted with grey in the adult; the young are spotted with white. An average male stands twenty inches at the shoulder and two inches taller at the rump; the hind limbs are longer than the front limbs. The head and body measure about three feet, not counting the tiny stubby tail. The animal weighs twenty to twenty-five pounds.

THE CHINESE WATER DEER

Worthy of passing mention at this point is the Chinese Water Deer, *Hydropotes inermis*, a dweller in the reed beds and low brush country along the shores and islands of the Yangtze River in China, and in Korea. A small creature without antlers, it is much like the musk deer in appearance. It may give birth to five or six young at a time—whereas one or two fawns are the rule among other deer.

THE VIRGINIA DEER WEARS A SPOTTED COAT WHEN YOUNG

The young fawn, too weak to travel about with its mother, is left behind by her when she goes off in search of food. Until she returns, the youngster remains hidden among rocks or tall grass, where its spotted coat helps to camouflage it. Every four hours or so the mother comes back to nurse her baby. When it is about five months old, the Virginia deer loses its spots.

See page 731.

DEER IN COMBAT

A pair of bucks spar, more in play than in earnest. In the mating season their battles are serious, for then they fight for the possession of a doe. *See page 710.*

WINTER HERD

Whitetail deer spend the winter in sheltered lowlands, but food is scarce and many starve. Note the three albinos in this herd. *See page 73!.*

Wisconsin Conservation Dept.

While the young of nearly all deer are born with white mottling, the extremely graceful axis deer of the Indian plains keeps its spots for life. Not large, but by no means the smallest of the family, axis deer love company and travel in mixed herds throughout the year.
See page 717

[6-9]

[6-9A]

Largest of the round-antlered deer, the American wapiti or elk formerly ranged over most of the United States and southern Canada, but today it is found only in the Rocky Mountains and Far West. A powerful bull may collect 50 or 60 cows in his harem but the young bachelors will either outbattle or outmanoeuvre him, so that the average number is 12.
See page 726

Although most deer are herd animals, the white-tailed or Virginia deer prefers its own company and never gathers in groups of more than two or three. Most abundant in the north-eastern United States, the white-tail is found throughout North America, Mexico and South America to Peru and Bolivia, living always on the edge of heavy forest land with easy access to open meadows.

See page 737

[6-10]

THE MUNTJAK, OR BARKING DEER

The Muntjak, or Barking Deer, *Muntiacus*, is also known as the Jungle Sheep, Red Hog-Deer, and Rib-faced Deer. A small animal, it is rather like the musk deer in size. However, it differs from other deer in a curious feature—the male has tusklike upper canine teeth. Timid and shy, this deer nevertheless makes good use of its long and well-developed canines in fighting off dogs and other natural enemies.

These canine teeth, one notes with interest, are not fixed firmly in the jaw; the muntjak is capable of moving them at will. Some observers believe that the peculiar rattling noise made by several animals together, while on the run, may be produced by the teeth.

Muntjak hunting is a popular sport in southern Asia, and this deer's flesh is considered excellent eating. The muntjak, though a solitary creature, may be attracted in small numbers to one area by the presence of food. However, it keeps close to dense cover and is difficult to shoot.

Wintertime is the favoured season for hunting the muntjaks—the natives line one side of a bushy area, and dogs are turned in from the other side and drive the animals toward the hunters. The muntjaks will make a fast getaway, if the hunter is not alert. These deer carry the head and neck low when running, and have a rather ungainly gait.

The muntjak utters a sharp, doglike bark—whence the name "barking deer". The call is often repeated, usually in the early morning or evening and sometimes after dark. The "bark", very loud for an animal the size of the muntjak, is uttered as a mating call or as a cry of alarm.

The rutting season in northern India for these deer is in January or February. Six months later, a single fawn is born; sometimes there are twins. The young are spotted at birth and retain their spotted coats until the following year.

The muntjak's two-pronged antlers, five or six inches long, grow from the top of high column-like bases covered with hair. The male drops his horns in May, and the new set is fully grown in August. The muntjak has an exceptionally long, extendible tongue, and can lick the whole of its face with it.

This animal's general colour varies from chestnut to tawny or mahogany red. The average shoulder height is two feet at most, with a head-and-body length of three feet as the maximum. Its weight is about twenty-eight pounds.

FALLOW DEER—AT HOME IN EUROPE'S PARKS AND RESERVES

The Fallow Deer, *Dama dama*, assembles in large herds in parks and open game reserves. In the wild, however, it is more likely to roam in small parties and hide in thickets during the daytime. While it eats a considerable amount of grass, it also browses on shoots, leaves, shrubs, and the like.

Fallow deer are quick to make up their minds to move. When they

ANTLERS WITH HANDLIKE TIPS

The fallow deer, denizen of Europe's parks and forests, has broad, flat antlers that end in the shape of a hand with small outspread fingers. A fascinating fact about antlers is that these elaborate structures—found only on the male—are shed in late winter and then grow back again before autumn, year in, year out. At first the antlers are soft and spongy; later the soft outer covering or "velvet" peels off or is rubbed off, as the antlers take on the bony hardness we usually associate with them.

are about to run, they shake their tails and then take off with a long, swinging trot. They can jump and scramble over a seven-foot fence. The animals are wary and hard to track.

Mating takes place about October and lasts one month. At this time you can hear the rutting cry of the fallow deer—deep-toned grunts or barks—a good two miles away. When they utter the cry, the neck is stretched out and the head, lower than normal, is jerked upward.

The calf comes in June. Usually there is only one; twins are rare, and there are never more than two. The doe does not show much concern for her fawn—on being alarmed, she either takes the fawn with her or else hides it in a thicket and gallops off without a backward look. The fawn gains the use of its legs much quicker than most other deer.

The fallow deer's antlers are broadly flattened, or palmate (stretched out like the fingers of the hand) at the tips; they are ornamented with several small tines. The colour of the typical animal is fawn dappled with whitish spots in summer, and uniformly greyish in winter; there are times when the entire animal is blackish brown. A large buck stands three feet at the shoulder and weighs about two hundred pounds.

The fallow deer started in the Mediterranean countries, but it has been introduced all over Europe. It is said to have been imported into Britain by the Romans, and the ancient Egyptians brought it to their own land.

AXIS DEER—GRACEFUL CREATURES OF INDIA

The Axis Deer, Spotted Deer, or Chital, *Axis axis*, is perhaps the most beautifully marked of all the family and is also one of the most graceful of all deer. Partial to surroundings of bushes and trees near water or in the bamboo jungles, it is a creature of the wild and beautiful scenery of the Indian plains and foothills; here, in a wonderland of rippling streams bordered by lofty trees, it wanders among open, grassy glades.

These spotted creatures love company. They associate in herds at all times of the year, and often several hundred are seen together. They favour daylight hours for their activities. Usually they go to drink between eight and ten o'clock in the morning, and sleep away the midday hours. Good swimmers, the animals readily take to water.

Their mating call is a loud, hoarse, barking sound, easy to recognize but impossible to describe. When startled they give voice to a shrill cry of alarm.

The axis deer is reddish brown in colour and profusely dappled with white spots which it keeps for life. It stands about three feet at the shoulder and weighs two hundred pounds or so. The antlers—they may measure up to three feet in length—are supported on short bases. Usually they have only two tines on each side.

DISTINCTIVE FOR ITS BEAUTIFUL COAT
The axis deer of India has an elegant chestnut coat, heavily dappled with white, which gives it an unusually colourful appearance. Like all ruminants, deer have a unique "delayed action" method of digesting food. The food is swallowed, next stored and softened in a special section of the stomach. Later, at the animal's convenience, it is brought up into the mouth as a cud, chewed, and re-swallowed—this time to be completely digested. Oxen, sheep, goats, antelopes, and giraffes also dine in this way.

The Hog Deer is a somewhat smaller animal. In India and Burma it is reddish brown, spotted with white in the young. The Eastern Hog Deer of Thailand, Cambodia, Annam, and Cochin China has an unspotted reddish-brown coat. Hog deer are comparatively unsocial and travel in groups of no more than two or three. At most the hog deer is twenty-nine inches at the shoulder; the buck has long, slender, three-pointed antlers.

SAMBAR DEER—DEER THAT WALLOW

The Sambar Deer, or Rusine Deer, *Cervus* (*Rusa*) *unicolor*, the common deer of south-eastern Asia and also the largest, is a forest or woodland creature. It may come out on grassy slopes or open forest glades to feed, but it quickly takes refuge among the trees when danger threatens.

Sambar deer never associate in large herds. Two or three and sometimes half a dozen animals are seen together; stags as well as hinds are often found singly. Hunted on horseback, they maintain a steady but not swift pace, and can easily be overtaken by a good horse in open country.

Grass is the sambar's favourite food, but it also browses on shoots and leaves of trees and often travels long distances to drinking places. It does most of its feeding in the early morning and evening. During the day it lies up in the forest, where it chooses a spot well shaded from the sun's rays.

SAMBARS DREAD INSECTS

The sambar is one of the few members of the deer family that make a habit of wallowing in mud holes like buffaloes and pigs. The animal probably developed this practice to protect itself against insect pests, especially flies. Living as the sambar does in the low, hot tropical jungles, it suffers greatly from these tormentors, particularly after the rains. It is curious that the wallowing habit seems to be limited to the stag; rarely is the hind found in a wallow.

THE MATING CALL

The sambar stag's mating call is a loud, somewhat metallic-sounding bellow. The hind's note is fainter and sharper. October and November are the months of the rutting season. A powerful stag usually appropriates two or three hinds, guarding them jealously from other stags until the mating season is over. Soon afterward, he drops his antlers (they are three-pointed like those of the hog deer).

Eight months after mating time, the hind retires to some secluded thicket in the forest and gives birth to a fawn. For her to have more than one young at a time is a rare occurrence. The young are without spots. In adults the hair is coarse and uniformly dark smoky brown in colour.

COMMONEST AND LARGEST DEER OF SOUTHERN ASIA

Like buffalo and pigs, but utterly unlike most other deer, the sambar or rusine deer wallows in mudholes, probably to give itself a protective coating against the insect pests so abundant in the jungle where it lives. This typical Asian deer has a sombre-coloured coat of coarse brown hair, and massive horns that are long and forked.

We find a number of varieties of the sambar living in different places at elevations of from four thousand to fourteen thousand feet in southern Asia. They vary in size, the largest being the Indian Sambar, which is also found in Ceylon. It stands over five feet at the shoulders and weighs six hundred pounds; its horns measure forty-eight inches in length.

SIKAS—DEER WITH PRECIOUS ANTLERS

The Sika, or Spotted Deer of East Asia, *Cervus* (*sika*) *nippon*, is a relatively small deer, lightly spotted, and marked with a light rump patch. We find this handsome animal in Manchuria and along the eastern coast of Asia, as well as on the offshore islands from Formosa to Japan. Subspecies are numerous.

ANTLERS FOR MEDICINE

The sika's antlers, which usually have four tines, are in great demand in the growing stage. The Chinese, who consider them more valuable for medicine than those of other deer, gladly pay high prices for them. In fact, the antlers have been known to bring a price of eighty Mexican dollars an ounce. Constant hunting has made the sika deer exceedingly shy.

THE ELUSIVE SIKA

Up until a hundred years ago, some sika species were almost unknown to the West. Père David, an indefatigable naturalist of the last century, heard of a new kind of sika in China and undertook to obtain a specimen.

At length his efforts were successful; but a mandarin who disliked foreigners had him arrested and confiscated the animal. In 1867, David's hunters secured a second sika, which was seized by Chinese officials and cut to pieces. However, the resourceful David salvaged the pieces and sent them to France. Scientists call this species *Cervus mandarinus* to commemorate the destructiveness of the Chinese officials.

The sika deer stands about three feet high at the shoulder and has a head-and-body length of about four feet, plus an eight-inch tail. Its chestnut summer coat is beautifully spotted with white; in winter, the colour changes to dull brown and the spots fade and almost disappear.

Schomburgk's Deer is native to the plains of Thailand and may occur in Yunnan, China. The antlers divide into nine or ten prongs, with the long, forked brow tine extending at right angles forward from the main beam. The body colour of this large deer is uniformly brown on the back and white beneath.

THAMIN AND SWAMP DEER

The Thamin, or Eld's Deer, *Cervus* (*Rucervus*) *eldi*, is a herd deer inhabiting grassy plains and swamps in groups of as many as fifty. They frequent the outskirts of the forest during the heat of the day; at other times they generally keep to more open country.

OFTEN BLINDED IN FIGHTING

Pugnacious by nature, the thamin or brow-antlered deer frequently pays for its fights by losing one or both eyes. Through its sense of hearing, a blinded stag can follow a herd and survive safely; once it is separated from the herd, however, it does not last long.

Known also as the Panolia Deer and the Brow-antlered Deer, the thamin reaches forty-five inches at the shoulder and weighs about 240 pounds. The large antlers have long brow tines, with from two or three to ten points branching from the main beam. The adult wears a brown coat with no contrasting markings. The spotted young—there usually is but one—is born in the late autumn and reaches its prime when six or seven years old. The typical thamin is found in Burma and the Malay Peninsula.

The Indian Swamp Deer, or Barasingha, *Cervus* (*Rucervus*) *duvaucelli*, despite the first of its names, is not a denizen of marshlands.

Instead, it favours open forests and grassy plains in northern India, where it gathers in large herds during the breeding season.

This animal is a proud-looking, massive creature. It stands four feet at the shoulder and weighs up to 560 pounds. Its handsome antlers, sometimes more than three feet long, bear from ten to sixteen points. In summer it sports a light reddish coat, more or less spotted with white; in wintertime the colour changes to yellowish brown.

RED DEER—FAMOUS FOR THEIR GOOD LOOKS

The Red Deer, *Cervus elaphus*, though it lacks the handsomely spotted coat of the axis deer, is considered by naturalists to be among the finest of the deer family. A larger animal, it is sleek, clean-cut, and well proportioned in build. Alert and lordly in bearing, it moves with striking grace. Its appearance is enhanced by an imposing crown of branched antlers. In short, this creature is in many ways the beau ideal among deer.

We find the red deer in many parts of the Old World: in Europe, Asia, and Africa. Its coat is reddish brown in summer, taking on a greyish tinge in winter. A large pale-buff patch marks the rump and extends along the sides of the tail. The full-grown stag stands about four feet at the shoulder and weighs three hundred pounds or more.

ANTLER LORE

In its prime, the stag normally carries six tines on each beam of the antlers—some, in fact, have been found with a far greater number of points. About one in every hundred stags never develops horns; we call such an individual a "hummel" or a "notts". Stags with only a brow tine and one terminal point are known as "switch-horns". Adult stags lose their antlers by March, but a new growth starts almost at once. By autumn, the replacements are fully formed and ready for use in combat.

As we have seen, an average red deer stag in his prime will carry six tines on each beam. The lowest tine over a deer's forehead is called the "brow" tine; the second tine is the "bez", the third the "trez", and the three remaining tines at the top forming a cup are the "sur-royals". A stag with six tines on each antler is a "Royal Hart", with a total of fourteen points or more it is a "Wilson" or "Imperial".

There is a whole lore and terminology for the deer in England. A barren female is known as a "yeld hind". A two-year-old male is called a "knobber"—with its first horns it is known as a "brocket". A stag in its fourth year is called a "staggart".

THE MATING SEASON

The red deer is a herd animal, but the males and females live apart except during the brief rutting season. The hinds and their offspring form closely knit groups—here we see the workings of the maternal instinct—and are not given to wandering like the males.

Shortly before the breeding season, which opens about September, the stags gather in large, rather loosely organized bands. Playfully they cavort about as they engage in seemingly good-natured fun and mock battles.

Sometimes the whole band will romp as a unit. But once rutting begins, the swollen-necked stags struggle savagely for possession of as many hinds as they can gather. It is only during the mating season, and after, that the males utter their defiant roars of jealousy and anger.

RANGE

Usually stags do not range over more than a mile or so of their domain, but during the search for females they run at a pace of six miles an hour and cover ten to twenty miles in a day. Once rutting is over, the bands settle down to another year of peaceful association.

FEMALE LEADERS

You may often see the stag pictured as "monarch of the glen", but this is far from the truth—he is not even the leader of the herd. A mature female, old in years but young enough to have her annual calf, is at the head of the band. Her followers are usually her own offspring and the descendants of her calves. When the lead hind stops breeding regularly, she soon loses her authority over the herd.

The hind has a sharp staccato bark, which is a danger signal sounded only by the herd leader. Upon hearing it, the band immediately halts all activity, standing silent and alert. This watchfulness lasts until the matriarch resumes normal behaviour by way of signifying that the danger is past. The moment she moves, the entire assemblage quietly follows.

Once a year, it is true, a stag rounds up each herd of hinds during the rut. But this herd male is merely a temporary policeman who drives away any presumptuous and over-ambitious rivals for his harem.

FROLICSOME YOUNGSTERS

Among red deer, the hind gives birth to her young about eight months after mating. The white-spotted offspring, usually a single fawn—rarely twins—is born in the spring.

Although the baby is able to stand and move immediately after

HANDSOME PRINCE OF THE DEER FAMILY

The red deer, common in temperate Asia and Europe, and especially associated with the Scottish Highlands, stands out as one of the most graceful and elegantly proportioned of all deer. Except at mating time, the sexes live apart. The stags wander off, unmindful of family ties; the affectionate and deeply maternal hinds form small bands, consisting of one matriarch leading her grown offspring and their fawns.

birth, it remains in the bush, where the affectionate mother has concealed it. The hind never wanders very far from her fawn but returns from time to time to nurse it.

As they become more active, fawns, like the young of many animals, romp and amuse themselves by playing such games as "tag" and "king of the castle". Foot races and make-believe battles, friendly but none the less strenuously contested, are favourite pastimes. The young harts and does indulge in an endless variety of springs, bounces, and laughably ridiculous posturings and twistings as they vie with each other in showing off.

MANY KINDS OF RED DEER

The red deer group consists of many species, subspecies, and varieties that differ according to where they live—the British Isles, continental Europe, Asia Minor, Asia proper, and the Mediterranean region of North Africa.

The comely appearance and gentle nature of these beasts make them general favourites among the great parks and forest preserves of the Old World. The Eastern species tend to have a greyer coat than the European types, with large amounts of black on the shoulders, thighs, and under-parts. Two varieties worthy of passing mention are the Maral Stag of the Caspian region and the Hangul Stag of the Kashmir valley.

The maral stag (or Persian red deer) is larger than its European cousin, standing four and one-half feet at the shoulder and weighing 560 pounds.

As for the hangul, it is often erroneously referred to as the bara-singha, a name which properly belongs to the Indian swamp deer. The hangul measures over four feet at the shoulder and weighs 450 pounds. It is a magnificent beast with branching antlers—like those of the European red deer—that may reach a length of fifty inches.

WAPITI—GIANTS OF THE TALL MOUNTAIN TIMBER

The American Wapiti, *Cervus canadensis*, better known in the United States as the Elk ("wapiti" is the name the Shawnee Indians gave it), is the largest of the round-antlered deer. With the exception of the moose, the wapiti is the largest deer alive in the world today. A full-grown wapiti stands five feet four inches at the shoulder and weighs from seven hundred to one thousand pounds. The antlers of the adult bull may have as much as a five-foot spread.

FIGHTING FOR A HAREM

The wapiti haunts the tall mountain timber. The sound of the clear "bugle call" by the bull at the beginning of the rutting season in the autumn is a challenge to battle with any other male in the neighbourhood. Starting in a low, stirring key and rising to a high pitch, it drops abruptly into a harsh scream, followed by a few grunts. An aggressive contender usually answers with a loud, defiant bark and the struggle is on.

In combat the bulls, with their necks swollen and their nostrils

THE WAPITI—BIG AMERICAN COUSIN OF THE RED DEER

The second largest deer in the world after the moose is the American wapiti, or elk, as it is known in the United States; it may weigh up to one thousand pounds. During the mating season, bulls are noted for their fierce battles, in which the victor acquires a harem of cows. Soon, however, bachelor stags appear, to taunt the leader into fighting again for his hard-won gains. Elk teeth were formerly in great demand, and for this reason alone the wapiti used to be slain in large numbers.

distended, rush full tilt and crash into each other, their horns rattling like swords. Occasionally a bull gets his neck broken by the force of the terrific impact. More often, however, one or the other realizes his inferiority after two or three battering passes. Accepting defeat, he gallops away.

Though a powerful bull may number fifty or sixty cows in his harem, a dozen females is the usual retinue. The point is that while an especially powerful stag may collect a large harem of cows for himself, he can rarely keep it very long. Several unmated bachelor stags usually manage to outmanoeuvre him. At first, to be sure, he is too cautious to be enticed into an all-out brawl by covetous stags; but eventually the taunts of one aspiring competitor will draw the head stag into a fast and furious battle. While he is thus engaged, other stags move in from different directions, split up the herd of cows into small groups, and quickly take them off to the hills. The old stag may win his battle, but his harem is gone and he is too exhausted to follow.

Were it not for such stratagems, the polygamous practices of the herd bull would leave a large number of stags unmated. Their natural instincts would have to go unsatisfied because of the ceaseless vigilance and physical superiority of the master of the harem.

WAPITI ENEMIES

The wolf, coyote, cougar, and bear are natural enemies of the elk. As a rule, a bull elk in possession of his formidable antlers is usually safe from attack by these predatory creatures.

In one combat, according to an eye witness report, a bear, caught by the savage charge of a maddened wapiti, was pierced through and through by the sharp, many-pronged antlers. Finally nothing remained of the bear but a butchered, gory hulk. The victor's rage was still not appeased. Before turning away into the forest, the elk reduced the body of his victim to an unrecognizable pulp by furiously stamping upon it with his forefeet.

THE LIFE OF A YOUNG WAPITI

The young elk arrives in May or June; it is usually born in open grassland. Within an hour, at most, after birth, the calf (generally there is only one) is not only able to stand—it can even walk on its wobbly legs! At first its coat is light tawny-brown with large white spots, an effectively inconspicuous pattern among the patches of brilliant light and deep shadow of the woodlands.

A few days after birth, the calf is strong enough to follow the main herd toward the summer range. The mother nurses her baby for the first six weeks, but after that it learns to browse on leaves and twigs. By August, the spots have faded, and late autumn finds the calves completely weaned. The animals average a life span of fifteen or sixteen years—in exceptional instances, twenty-two years.

WHERE THEY LIVE

Throughout the summer, herds of elk live high up in the mountains, where they are free from attack by mosquitoes and other insect pests. When autumn comes, they descend to lower altitudes, spending the winter in the sheltered valleys and meadows.

Originally the wapiti ranged over most of the United States and southern Canada. Today we find it only in the Rocky Mountain region and the Far West. The closely related wapiti of central and eastern Asia are now included with the red deer groups.

As for the American wapiti, its general body colour is pale fawn, but the head and the maned neck are dark chestnut-brown. The large rump patch and short tail are straw-coloured. The tremendous antlers have more than five well-developed tines in the adult.

PERE DAVID'S DEER AND THEIR STRANGE ANTLERS

Père David's Deer, or Milu, *Elaphurus davidianus*, is a strange animal to the Chinese way of thinking. They call it *Ssu-ou-hsiang*, "the four unlikes". As they put it, this deer has the tail of an ass, the hoofs of a cow, the neck of a camel, and the antlers of a stag!

MYSTERIOUS ANTLERS

The antlers of Père David's deer are peculiar in that the front branch comes off fairly high above the base and is usually forked once and sometimes twice. The hind prong is long, slender, and straight, often with small branches at the extremity.

But what is much more remarkable about these antlers is that we have some evidence to indicate that fully adult Père David's deer may actually grow two sets of antlers within a single year—a summer set and a winter set. Up until they reach maturity, the stags have only one set. When they have two, the antlers are smaller.

Mature stags shed their summer antlers immediately after the rut, at the beginning of November, but sometimes as early as September. The shedding of the winter antlers varies a great deal among individuals. Still, no matter how late the animal drops its winter antlers, the new set, even if only partly grown, will harden in time for the mating season in the autumn.

EXTINCT IN THE WILD

Known in captivity only, the rare and unusual Père David's deer of China cannot be found anywhere but in private parks and in zoos—a French naturalist discovered it in the gardens of the summer palace at Peking, where it had apparently long outlived its ancestors in the wild. This animal's antlers are an oddity of the deer world; instead of the customary single set, the adult stag often grows two sets each year—one in the summer and one in winter. Père David's deer likes water—it wades and swims, given the opportunity.

This peculiar trait may be a hangover from past generations when these deer possibly bred twice a year—a new development in the deer family or merely a sport of nature. It is noteworthy that older stags, with their small antlers, cannot compete with the younger animals, whose single set is larger.

The white-tail fawn is usually born in May when, especially in northern and eastern districts, the flowering shrubs combine with its spotted coat to help camouflage it from its many enemies. With a life expectancy of from 15 to 20 years, one doe may give birth to more than 30 fawns.

[6-11]

See page 731

[6-11A]

A white-tail buck "in velvet". Deer shed their antlers during the winter or early spring, and a new growth begins almost immediately. During the growing period the antlers are soft and spongy, covered with a downy fur, but once growth stops they harden to bonelike consistency and the "velvet" peels off.

See page 731

The Columbia black-tailed deer lives on the Pacific Coast ranging from central British Columbia to California. It never ventures inland beyond the Sierra Nevadas and Cascade Mountains, but it has been seen swimming three miles offshore—in a heavy sea.
See page 735

[6-13]

Mule deer (the Columbia is one variety) get their name from their large ears, which are fairly uncommon in the deer family. All natives of western North America, these deer replace their tawny summer coat with longer, greyer hair in winter. The tip of the tail is always black.
See page 734

[6-13A]

Largest and most uncouth of living deer, the moose has disproportionately long legs. This young bull will add almost a half a ton to his weight as he matures, but his gangling legs will always seem "wrong". *See page 739*

[6-14]

Of the three or four varieties of moose spread across North America from Maine to the Rockies and through Canada to Alaska, the largest and most powerful is the Alaskan moose. Although the bull's broad-tined antlers may weigh 60 pounds and spread more than 70 inches, they are shed and replaced each year.
See page 742

A Wyoming moose demonstrates one advantage of his long legs: wading into deep water to feed on water lilies, a moose delicacy. With their short necks moose cannot eat short grass unless they kneel, and in order to drink they must wade into the water.   *See page 739*

[6-14A]

APPROACHING EXTINCTION

The reason for this peculiarity will never be solved, as Père David's deer is on the verge of extinction. The few animals now in captivity, however, seem to be increasing the tendency to have two sets of antlers each year. These deer were brought to the attention of the West by the French naturalist Père David, already referred to, who saw a herd of them in the gardens of the Summer Palace at Peking. They had been royal property for a very long time; no one seemed to know exactly where they came from.

BRED PRIVATELY

Today this extremely rare deer is being bred only in a few private parks and zoological gardens. Naturalists believe that the animal originally dwelt in the swampy, reed-covered plains that once existed over the greater part of north-eastern China. However, they have never succeeded in discovering it in the wild.

Père David's deer is large—three feet, nine inches at the shoulder—with a bushy tail longer than that of other deer. Its moderately small ears are well haired on the inside.

The winter coat is dull greyish buff, and the young are spotted with white as are most deer fawns.

WHITE-TAILED DEER—THEY CARRY A "SIGNAL FLAG"

The White-tailed Deer, or Virginia Deer, *Odocoileus virginianus*, is a creature of the American woodlands. However, instead of frequenting deep, unbroken forest, it chooses to live where dense woods and thickets alternate with open meadow and sunny forest glades. A shy, secretive animal, it never gathers in groups of more than two or three.

At the approach of danger, the white-tailed deer will silently steal away, with head lowered and "white flag" (the tail) held down tight. The moment the deer starts to run, it throws caution to the winds and carries its tail aloft, waving from side to side—an unmistakable sign of warning for its fellows.

The white-tailed deer is not much of a migrator, and it prefers its own company to that of a herd. About three hundred acres is the extent of this more or less solitary animal's home territory.

DEER *versus* RATTLESNAKE

The deer and the rattlesnake are confirmed enemies. Many a mortal combat has taken place between the buzzing reptile and the antlered monarch.

A battle between a snake and a deer is a dramatic spectacle. With head lowered and held sideways for better vision, the buck warily approaches its foe and receives the lunging strike of the snake on its horns. In a flash, the deer springs into the air and lands with all four sharp hoofed feet on the rattler, instantly bounding off to repeat the manoeuvre. After a few such onslaughts, the snake is literally cut to ribbons.

Though she lacks antlers, the doe attacks in much the same fashion as the buck.

IT RUNS WITH TAIL ALOFT

Seen above in typical motion is the white-tailed or Virginia deer. Small and fleet-footed, it follows an unbeaten trail through thickets and woodland, leaping high over fallen logs, waving its long white-bottomed tail. Once the deer is in its stride, it carries the tail straight. The animal is an unwelcome sight in any orchard—it strips the trees of fruit, twigs, and leaves.

WHITE-TAIL COURTING AND FAMILY LIFE

The bucks start courting the does in October, and the mating season lasts until December. There are fierce fights between the bucks for possession of the does. Frequently their antlers become inseparably locked together and both animals starve to death.

The spotted fawns are usually born in May and weigh about four pounds apiece. The number of young to each doe varies according to the mother's age. Her first-born is single; the second year she may have twins and sometimes triplets. Occasionally there are four—though this is rare for any deer.

The white-tailed deer has a life expectancy of fif een to twenty years, and a doe may have as many as thirty-one fawns during the first fourteen years of her life.

THE FAR-RANGING WHITE-TAIL

Though most abundant in the north-eastern United States, the white-tailed deer ranges over the whole width of North America from southern Canada through Mexico, and down into South America as far as Peru and Bolivia.

This deer is rather small and graceful. It is also known as the "fan-tailed deer", and its long, bushy tail is conspicuously white on the underside. The back, sides, and limbs of the summer coat are uniformly tawny in colour, while the heavier winter dress is more sombre and greyish in tone. In both coats the undersides and throat are white.

VARIETY IN SIZE

We find a great deal of difference among the more than a dozen kinds of white-tailed deer, not to mention the numerous local varieties. The more northern of these are among the largest and may reach sixty-six inches in head-and-body length, with a shoulder height of forty-six inches. The full-grown buck ranges from two hundred to four hundred pounds in weight.

By way of contrast there is the Dwarf White-tailed Deer, measuring only fifty inches from its nose to the root of its tail and weighing less than fifty pounds. The main beam of the antlers in all the white-tailed deer curves forward and the tip inward, giving off two or more erect, unbranched tines.

MULE DEER—NAMED FROM THEIR BIG EARS

The Mule Deer, *Odocoileus hemionus,* is a sociable creature. It follows regular migration routes, spending the warm summer months in the mountains and moving to the sheltered valleys and lower levels in the autumn. During such seasonal movements, the combined herds on the trails may number several hundred animals.

A FRIENDLY BUT MUCH-HUNTED FELLOW

The mule deer, named after that other possessor of large ears, is well known in the western part of North America. Hunters value it as food; visitors to national parks find it extremely sociable, and enjoy feeding it out of their hands.

Since the mating season is in the late autumn, the fawns are born on the way back to the summer range. The does have their babies— usually twins—six or seven months after mating. There is one instance of a marked doe that gave birth to twins for twenty successive years before becoming barren.

The mule deer has large ears—hence its name. Its appearance is quite different from the white-tailed deer's in this way, and in many others.

The mule deer has a large whitish rump patch, but the tip of the rather short tail is black. The antlers rise vertically from the head and are evenly divided at the first fork; each tine again divides to produce four or more evenly spaced spikes on each antler.

In summer this animal's coat is tawny or yellowish brown in colour; in winter, it is much longer and greyer. An adult buck may stand forty-two inches at the shoulder and measure about sixty inches in length, not including the eight-inch tail. Its weight runs from 150 to two hundred pounds.

There are about a dozen kinds of mule deer, each specializing in its own area, which may be rather large. Occasionally these territories overlap to some extent.

The domain of the mule deer is western North America, from northern Mexico to central British Columbia, and from Colorado in the east to California in the west. The extremes in range are represented by the Southern Mule Deer, an animal that roams Baja California, and the Sitka Deer, found on coastal ranges and islands from north of Juneau, Alaska, to central British Columbia. The Columbia Black-tailed Deer, of the Pacific coast, is still another well-known type.

COLUMBIA BLACK-TAILED DEER—
CREATURES WITH COURAGE

The black-tail, like other mule deer, does not lack courage and will sell its life dearly, as shown by a mute picture which met the eyes of a United States Biological Survey man. The skeletons of a large buck black-tail and a full-grown mountain lion were found lying side by side in a hemlock grove in Oregon. There was evidence of a violent struggle. A round hole in the top of the lion's skull had apparently been made by a prong of the deer's antlers—proof that though the deer had lost its fight for freedom, it had mortally wounded the lion in the conflict.

The Columbia black-tailed deer has a longer range than the Sitka deer—it occupies a narrow strip along the Pacific coast from central British Columbia to California. Nowhere does the black-tail range inland beyond the Sierra Nevadas and the Cascade Mountains. It is easy to recognize the Columbia black-tail and the Sitka deer by the rather long tail, black on the upper surface, and by the forked antlers, which have two main tines of equal size.

These small animals are apparently good swimmers; they have been seen three miles offshore in a heavy sea, headed across Frederick Sound, which is ten miles wide.

CENTRAL AND SOUTH AMERICAN DEER

The Brocket, or Cariacu, *Mazama,* may be encountered all the way from Veracruz, Mexico, through Central America, and into South America. It has short, unbranched spike antlers about half as long as the head. All members of the brocket group are small, stocky deer— the average shoulder height is about two feet. The Pygmy Brocket of

SHORT HORNS ON A SHORT DEER

Though its body is small and squat, and its diminutive antlers are devoid of forks and branches, the brocket or cariacu of South and Central America is nevertheless a true member of the deer family. There is even a pygmy brocket, which stands less than nineteen inches at the shoulder—almost the smallest deer on record.

central Brazil ranks among the smallest of all true deer, standing less than nineteen inches at the shoulder. The body colour of these animals is basically brown.

——ALERT, SHY, RETIRING. Brockets are at home in the dense thickets of unbroken forests from sea-level to altitudes of sixteen thousand feet. Like other deer, they are browsing animals and feed on leaves, twigs, and green shoots of trees or bushes.

Alert, shy, and retiring, brockets are most active during the early hours of the morning and late evening. Among the hosts of hungry predators ready to devour these timid beasts, big snakes and large cats take the greatest toll.

Brockets are not sociable creatures. They do not gather in herds; instead, a male and female usually join company. The average number of young for an adult doe is two. At birth the fawns are spotted with white. They are able to stand shortly after they come into the world, and in several days they are ready to accompany their parents.

There are at least seven recognized kinds of brockets, with a good many varying types among them. The best known is the Red Brocket of Central America.

The Andean Deer, Huemul, or Taruga, *Hippocamelus*, is a lover of the heights. The Peruvian Huemul is at home in the Andes at elevations of about three miles in Peru. Its relative the Chilean Huemul remains below the timber line of a range that extends through Chile and western Argentina nearly to the Strait of Magellan. Both have a very odd trait that does them a marked disservice.

——FAR FROM WARY. For some unexplained reason, huemuls appear to be unconcerned about their safety. Observers have testified on more than one occasion to the unusual lack of wariness on the part of these deer.

Thus, one reliable informant states that he walked in full view to within rifle distance of four huemuls, singled out the largest, then fired and missed. A second shot dropped one, but the other three did not run off—they merely stood as if amazed or slowly walked about in a curious, stiff goose-step manner. Meanwhile, a herd of guanacos that was on the same hillside had quickly disappeared over the top of the mountain at the first rifle crack.

Smaller in size than the typical white-tailed deer, the Andean deer has a shoulder height of thirty-nine inches. Its total length, including the five-inch tail, is sixty-six inches. Males carry heavy antlers, about ten inches long, consisting of one simple fork and two points on each side. The hair is rather coarse and thick in texture, and brownish or yellowish brown in colour.

TOO TRUSTING FOR ITS OWN SAFETY

The huemul or taruga lives at altitudes of from fourteen thousand to sixteen thousand feet in the Andes, from Peru to Chile. It is about the size of the Virginia deer and has short, massive antlers with a simple fork. The animal seems to lack the wariness common in most wild creatures, and easily falls victim to hunters.

The Marsh Deer, or Suasupucu, *Blastocerus dichotomus*, is the largest and handsomest deer in South America. A swamp-loving animal that ranges from Brazil to the forested country of Argentina, the marsh deer is about the size of a red deer. Its antlers may exceed twenty inches in length and fork into two equal branches that subdivide, forming ten points in all. The animal's general colour is reddish chestnut in summer and browner in winter.

The Pampas Deer, a relative of the marsh deer, lives on the pampas and prairies from Brazil to northern Patagonia. The Chilean Pudu, the smallest American deer, has a shoulder height of about thirteen inches, and weighs twenty-four pounds at most. It takes readily to salt water and crosses over to Chiloe Island off the Chilean coast. The gentle fawns are easily tamed.

BIGGEST OF SOUTH AMERICA'S DEER

The most attractive and the largest member of the deer family found in South America is the marsh deer. This animal makes its home in the forests from Brazil to Argentina, and shows a special fondness for dwelling in and about swamps.

MOOSE—GIANTS OF THE DEER FAMILY

The Moose, *Alces*, known in Europe as the "elk", is the largest living members of the deer family. Towering above the other animals of the northern latitudes, an average full-grown bull stands just under six feet at the shoulder and weighs between a thousand and fourteen hundred pounds. Exceptionally large moose antlers have been known to weigh sixty pounds.

PLAIN-LOOKING, CUMBROUS, AND UNCOUTH

There are some odd shapes and forms in the mammal world, and the moose, plain-looking, cumbrous, and uncouth, has one of them. The shoulders are higher than the rump. The legs seem much too long for the humpbacked body, and they are certainly too long for the short neck. In fact, a moose cannot reach down after short grass unless it kneels; in order to drink, it must wade into the water.

However, the long legs are useful to the moose in several ways. They enable the animal to reach high up to browse on twigs and leaves of willow trees, and to go into deep water to feed on water lilies—one of its favourite summer foods. At times, when feeding, a moose will wade into water so deep that it will become completely submerged. Finally, the long legs of the moose are well adapted for travel through the tangled masses of down timber (fallen timber) that would prove an impassable barrier to an animal with shorter limbs.

HUGE ANTLERS

Bulls have huge antlers, flattened and bearing numerous points, that may extend sideways from fifty to more than seventy inches. The

THE MONUMENTAL MOOSE

The famous moose is the largest and clumsiest-looking of all deer; its antlers alone may weigh up to sixty pounds. It has a strange, protruding muzzle and an odd mouth with a flexible, overhanging upper lip—well suited for feeding upon foliage. Not nearly so plentiful as it once was, the moose needs protection if it is to survive for long.

tail of the moose is a mere stump; the ears are large. The animal has a long head, with a bulbous nose and an ample, pendulous upper lip. Its coat is long, coarse, and blackish brown in colour, with greyish tones on the face, belly, and lower limbs. A growth of skin and long hair, known as the "bell", hangs from the animal's throat.

TERRIFIC BATTLES OF THE MATING SEASON

A solitary animal, the moose generally sticks to one mate. The rutting season occurs in the autumn, and the bulls fight terrific battles for possession of the cows. The effects of these mighty duels are visible in the forest for some time—trees are badly scarred, the ground is torn up.

The rut begins in September and lasts until the beginning of October. The calf comes into the world eight months later—in May or thereabouts. The cow moose usually has one baby the first season, but two are not unusual. On rare occasions three are born. Unlike many deer, the moose calf is not spotted or striped with white but resembles the mother in its nearly uniform coloration. How long the moose lives in the wild we cannot say for sure; in captivity it does not survive for longer than a year or two.

WHERE MOOSE EAT

The moose has an extensive domain. Spending the summer in low-lying swamps and lake districts, it turns in wintertime to hardwood mountain ridges. A creature of habit, it roams its domain over well-worn trails to favourite feeding grounds.

In summer, the moose is fond of pond weeds and lily pads. Its principal food in winter is the leaves, shoots, and tender branches of willows, striped maple, and witch hazel.

When the snow lies deep on the ground, the moose keeps short trails open by constant travel. These are known as "moose yards". Occasionally two or three animals will occupy the same clearing in the forest, and gradually extend the size of the yard as food gets scarce.

NEW WORLD AND OLD WORLD MOOSE

There are three or four varieties of North American moose which are distributed from the Rocky Mountain region to Maine and north through Canada and Alaska. The largest and most powerful of these is the Alaskan Moose, which may attain a shoulder height of eighty-one to ninety-six inches and a weight of eighteen hundred pounds.

THE CLOVEN HOOFPRINTS OF THE DEER
At the left are the delicate footprints of the white-tailed deer, often found near small ponds and lakes. At the right are the longer and more pointed tracks of the moose. Moose tracks are the largest made by any deer.

There are also three kinds of Old World moose. We find the typical European animal in the Scandinavian peninsula and Germany; the typical Siberian and Manchurian forms have an extensive Asiatic range. The antlers of the Old World animals are somewhat flattened; none can even approach the enormous spread of those of the Alaskan moose.

CARIBOU AND REINDEER—"CAMELS OF THE FROZEN NORTH"

Reindeer are far-famed creatures today. Their popularity, however, does not seem to go much farther back than a poem which begins with the memorable words "'Twas the night before Christmas," and introduces the fleet-footed companions of Saint Nicholas—Cupid, Vixen,

Comet, and the rest. Ever since Clement Moore wrote his warm-hearted verses in the last century, the reindeer of the far-off North have seemed near and dear to us.

These big beasts are not always so good-humoured as is commonly supposed. During the mating season, reindeer are in a fighting mood and extremely dangerous—the air resounds with the crash of their antlers. Many a man has been killed at this season of the year, when the bulls, or stags, battle for supremacy over the harems.

WILD AND DOMESTICATED REINDEER

Reindeer have been called the "Camels of the Frozen North". With the exception of the musk ox, they live farther north than any other hoofed animal; they range beyond the timber line into the Arctic Circle in both the New World and the Old World.

In the wild state, these animals are known as caribou. Today we find caribou chiefly in the New World, where there are Barren Ground Caribou, Woodland Caribou, and Mountain Caribou. There is also an Old World Caribou, known as the reindeer in its domesticated form. (The word "reindeer" appears originally to have meant an "animal that pastures".) Reindeer have been introduced into the New World, and have proved of the greatest value to the Eskimos as a source of food and clothing.

UNIQUE AND PICTURESQUE ANTLERS

The Caribou, *Rangifer*, is the only deer in which we find both sexes with antlers. Even the fawns have small spike antlers which appear two months after birth.

The antlers themselves are unique and picturesque. The main beams sweep gracefully back and upward from the head, spreading as they rise, then bend forward and end in a flattened palm.

The shape and number of tines vary quite a bit. The brow tine usually develops only on one antler and extends down over the face in a broad vertical palm or "shovel". It is generally supposed that the "shovel" is used to dig down through the snow to the underlying moss, on which the animal often feeds. Still, the caribou has more success digging with its feet. The bulls drop their antlers in the early winter; the does carry them until May.

BIG HERDS, LONG MIGRATIONS

The caribou is the most sociable, as well as the most migratory, of all deer. Some of the more northern groups begin to collect in August for the movement south. During the exodus from the open tundra to the shelter of the timber, some may travel several hundred miles. Often the migrating herds number thousands of animals.

When they are travelling, caribou produce a noticeable snapping or clicking sound. This is made by the ankle joints—not, as one might suppose, by the clacking, wide-spreading hoofs. The caribou has a fast-swinging trot that it can keep up almost indefinitely. To this trot it owes its ability to outdistance wolves with ease. An excellent swimmer, too, it can only be overtaken in the water by a first-rate canoeman.

Caribou virtually disappeared from the United States within the memory of some old-timers. The last native caribou in Maine (the wildest part of the north-eastern United States), took refuge at Mount Katahdin and was exterminated by 1901. Later, the animals were brought back by man. Caribou fared better in Michigan, where a small herd persists in the northern part of the state. In Mount McKinley National Park the creatures are breeding with reindeer.

Caribou are still abundant in the Canadian Rockies and in the Barren Grounds. Their number, however, was much greater in the past. "Buffalo" Jones, a famous hunter, reported seeing a migrating herd of caribou at Clinton-Colden (in north-western Canada) that will give you some idea of their former abundance. From where he stood, said Jones, the whole world seemed a moving mass of caribou, extending ten miles each way. They averaged at least one hundred to an acre and passed at a rate of three miles per hour, travelling day and night. Some herds took four days to pass a particular point.

The naturalist Ernest Thompson Seton estimated the number of caribou in this herd at not less than twenty-five million. He suggested that it was possible there were several herds of similar size in existence at that time.

THE CARIBOU'S ENEMIES

It has been said, and justly so, that, except for sex-maddened bulls, a caribou has never attacked man. This animal is a combination of curiosity and timidity. Once a caribou gets the scent of a man, it will make off at a fast trot. If he is not identified at once, the case is different. With the wind blowing away from it, a caribou will approach a stranger, coming closer and closer until it is ten or twenty yards away, sniffing and snorting. But, the moment it smells danger, off it goes.

On the Arctic tundra, the caribou has few natural foes. On rare occasions it encounters a grizzly, a lynx, or a wolverine. On the other hand, the great white Arctic wolf is a constant menace. In an open chase, the caribou generally outruns the wolf. However, by skulking undetected around the outskirts of a herd, the wolf can manoeuvre within striking distance of a young or infirm straggler.

Strange as it may seem, the most dreaded enemies of the caribou are the denizens of the insect world. Mosquitoes hover around the warm-blooded animals in dense clouds—the unfortunate caribou must be constantly on the move, headed into the wind. An even greater menace is the botfly or warble fly, which lays its eggs in the caribou's hide. In some regions, young bucks have been found with as many as 120 warble larvae growing on their bodies.

"In midsummer," writes Joseph Dixon, an expert with the United States Fish and Wild Life Service, "caribou often seek high, wind-swept ridges and snow-filled gulches in order to escape the attacks of biting flies and mosquitoes that are abundant in the lowlands. On such trips the bands frequently are led by some old female, probably because she knows where the best green pastures are located and where safety for the weak young caribou may be found.

"Caribou have a keen sense of smell but their eyesight is relatively poor. I have found it possible, by lying flat on the ground, to crawl slowly down a hill right into the midst of a band of grazing caribou when the wind was blowing from them to me and they could not get my scent. Under such circumstances it was always a female, usually one with a young calf, that first detected my presence."

A WOODLANDS JEST

John McGaw, a hunter, once witnessed a most surprising exhibition of playfulness between a caribou and a fox. While stalking two caribou on Serpentine Hills, near Gander, Newfoundland, he noticed that one of the stags was acting strangely and backing away from some small creature that was jumping up from the ground at its side.

On closer observation, McGaw saw that the curious little creature was a young fox apparently trying to engage the larger animal in a frolic. Repeatedly the fox jumped into the air, snapping its teeth when off the ground. Apparently resenting these manoeuvres, the stag charged. The fox skipped to the other side and repeated its sport.

The game went on for some time, the fox apparently enjoying the sport of teasing its clumsy friend, who did not seem to relish the joke in the slightest degree. Eventually, the merry little fox retreated to safety.

THE CARIBOU AS FOOD

Flesh of the caribou is among the choicest meats. It is the staple food of the northern Indian and Eskimo—without the herds of caribou they would perish. Indians of the Tinne tribe are known as "Caribou-eaters", Eskimos of the Barren Ground as "Caribou Eskimos".

The people of the northland make use of every part of the animal; even the blood, which goes into soup. The flesh consumed, the bones are crushed for marrow. The shin bone is split for knives, horns are fashioned into fishhooks, and tendons made into thread.

"Reindeer moss" (moss and lichen eaten by the caribou in winter) is indigestible to man in its natural form. However, digested by the caribou, it becomes a nutritious human food. It is taken from the caribou's stomach by the Far Northerners and called *nerrooks* or *nerrokak*. By their use of the caribou as food, Eskimos and Greenlanders seem to have entered the realm of the scientific dietitian.

[6-15]

The connection between this bull caribou of the Barren Grounds of Canada and "A Visit from St. Nicholas" is not apparent but there is one—he is a wild reindeer. Although primarily New World animals, one species of caribou does exist in the Old World and it too is known as reindeer in its domesticated form.

See page 743

Among antlered deer each buck sports the specifically patterned "crowning glory" of his particular variety. Of all does, only the caribou shares this adornment and, male or female, her fawn will sprout small spikes at the age of two months.

See page 743

[6-15A]

[6-16]

Within the memory of our living elders, herding caribou were counted by the million. Staff of life for the Eskimo and Northern Indian, near-sighted and addicted to travelling in the open—easy prey to hunters human and wolf—their numbers have been so reduced that today this herd estimated at 14,000 arouses excitement.   *See page 743*

[6-16A]

However much man and wolf may decimate their ranks, the most dreaded enemy of the caribou is an insect, the warble fly which lays its eggs in their hides. Their only defence from other insect pests, mosquitoes and flies is upwind, frantic flight.
See page 743

Fish and Their Fabulous Neighbours

"How do they stay in the water?" "How do they breathe?" "Can they hear?" "How long can they live?"

These are but a few of the questions that will occur to your child as he observes the goldfish or tropical fish in an aquarium at home or elsewhere. For fish are interesting, question-provoking creatures. Schools have recognized their popular appeal by making aquariums classroom projects. Newspapers may have features telling how to take care of tropical fish; whole magazines deal with the subject; and shows displaying the most unusual kinds of fish are attended by eager youngsters as well as grown-ups.

The common goldfish is the most popular among children, and even a young child can be taught to care for a few of these hardy, handsome creatures in an ordinary fish bowl before you enlarge the collection with tropical specimens.

So attractive are goldfish and the colourful natives of tropical waters, that interior decorators often plan space for aquariums in formal settings as well as in recreation rooms. But beauty is by no means the whole charm of these creatures. As we watch the fish behind glass walls, so tranquil and completely undisturbed by captivity, we have an experience comparable to donning a diving helmet and going into the sea to observe underwater life. Much of what we see and learn applies as well to the life of fish which cannot be observed so closely.

Now for some of the questions that a youngster, especially one learning to swim, may ask about fish.

"How does it just *stay there*?" he may inquire when he sees a fish motionless in the water. "Why doesn't it sink to the bottom or come to the top?"

THE SWIM BLADDER

The ability of some fish to stay quietly in one place is due to a unique organ known as the "swim bladder". It is in the forward part of the body and is filled with gas—a mixture of oxygen and nitrogen. Most fish (including the goldfish) that have skeletons of true bone possess this organ; they need very little fin movement to stay at a given depth. When they die, their bodies rise to the surface.

Sharks and some other kinds of fish have skeletons of gristle. They lack the swim bladder and consequently they can remain suspended in one position only by continuous muscular effort. When these fish die, their bodies sink instead of rising.

How Fish Breathe

A fish has very small nostrils which you can see if you look closely on either side of its snout. The nostrils lead to a little sac where the sense of smell is located—but they have no connection whatever with breathing. When you see a goldfish constantly opening and closing its mouth, it is seeking air or oxygen and not food. Though they live in water, fish need oxygen just as people do; but they need it in a different form. Most fish "drown" in the air just as a human being will under water if he is submerged too long.

HOW THE GILLS WORK

Instead of breathing through nostrils and lungs, a fish is equipped to breathe with gills. You can see its gill covers—flat, bony flaps—just behind its head, one on each side. When the fish opens its mouth, allowing water to flow in, the gill covers are pressed against the body so that water will not enter from behind them.

Then you see the gill covers move outward as the water is forced out through the gill slits when the mouth closes. As the water passes through, the oxygen that it contains is absorbed by the tiny blood vessels making up the gills. (At the same time these blood vessels give off carbon dioxide and other body wastes.) The new oxygen thus obtained is then circulated through the body.

What Fins Are For

As you watch your goldfish swimming you may get the idea that its fins are an important element in its forward movement. And you are right, though nowadays scientists do not attach as much value to the locomotion value of fins as they once did. Experiments have shown that a fish can navigate even without its fins.

You will note seven fins on the common goldfish. Just behind its gill covers it has a pair of fins called the pectorals. Farther back is another pair called the ventrals—or, if quite far forward, called the pelvics. On its back the fish has a dorsal fin, which it sometimes lifts and shuts down like a fan. On the underside, towards the tail, is the anal fin. Finally, at the end of the tail is the caudal fin; we often call it the tail fin.

HOW FINS HELP FISH TO SWIM

How the different kinds of fins aid a fish's movement depends on their shape and position. The caudal or tail fin helps the fish propel itself as it presses its tail against the water first to one side then to the other. The shape of this fin seems to be related to the swimming speed of different species. On swift swimmers, such as the trout, the caudal fin is strongly forked or moon-shaped; on slow swimmers this tail fin is blunt or rounded.

The dorsal fin acts as a keel: it prevents rolling. The anal fin serves the same purpose and in some species it is also used to give the fish a powerful upward sweep.

Pectoral fins appear to serve chiefly as brakes for fish with bony skeletons—this is particularly true of perch—and these fins also have a slight balancing effect. In fish with other than bony skeletons—and this makes an interesting contrast—the pectorals have a powerful balancing action but are of little use as brakes. Sharks, for example, are apparently unable to make a sudden stop. As for the ventral fins, they contribute further to keeping the fish evenly balanced.

The fins of the common goldfish are by no means standard equipment. Many fishes do not have ventrals. Some, like the cod, have three dorsal fins; others have two; others, one. Some have two anal fins; others, one.

Fascinating Fins. Certain kinds of fish have fascinatingly specialized uses for one or more of their fins. The front ray of the first dorsal fin of the angler fish is perfectly adapted as a rod and lure with which it fishes for smaller creatures to eat. A number of fish have fins modified into sucking pads, and some use specially adapted pectoral fins for walking on the bottom of the sea—or even on land!

MOVING THROUGH THE WATER

The fish's mastery of motion in the water is wonderful to behold. It can dart forward with tremendous speed, starting from a complete "standstill"; it can progress a fraction of an inch with scarcely

AN IMPORTANT FOODFISH

Carp originated in Asia, but have been introduced to all the other continents, and in some waters have become a nuisance. More carp than any other freshwater fish are eaten by man. Of these, vast numbers are reared in ponds in Europe and other parts of the world.

a motion; it can move straight up or down or backwards. There are three types of swimming motions, and most fish use all three. These are: a sinuous movement of the whole body, the movements of the fins, and the propulsion resulting from water being shot through the gill chambers.

Swimming Speeds. When your child sees his goldfish cover the length of its aquarium with one quick swish of its body in what seems like no time at all, he may get the impression that fish always move with notable speed. It is true that many species are capable of extremely rapid bursts of speed, but over long distances they average a much slower rate of speed.

Salmon may go at a rate of twenty-five miles an hour, whereas carp are not known to exceed seven and a half.

How the Goldfish Gets Its Colour

Goldfish owe much of their attractiveness to their golden sheen. "Is there really any gold in a goldfish?" a youngster looking at his aquarium may ask. The goldfish scales do resemble this precious metal, but of course there is no trace of gold in their shiny covering. Colour in fish is mainly the effect of pigments which for the most part are scattered in the surface layers of the skin and are visible through the scales.

The ancestors of goldfish were olive in colour. They belonged to the carp family and lived in the streams of China. Hundreds of years ago some specimens were found with golden tones on their sides, and breeding was started with these. The gold predominated in some of their offspring, and selective breeding continued until fish completely golden in colour were achieved.

About seventy-five years ago a sailor brought back some goldfish to America from the Orient. They have been popular pets in many countries ever since.

VARIETIES OF GOLDFISH

Today we see many fancy varieties, such as fantail, fringetail, telescope, and lion-head. The breeding of specially selected fish produces these highly ornamental creatures, though great numbers of "common" goldfish appear along with them. This type characteristically has a long body, forked tail, and small head. It may be all gold or marked with black and silver. It is hardier than its ornamental relatives, and if it is transferred to a pond with ample food it may grow to be a foot in length.

Fish Use Camouflage Too

The colour of fish is often a definite camouflage, comparable to protective schemes on many birds and mammals. You may see a hint of protective coloration in a goldfish, as the orange tones of its back fade to pale lemon-yellow below. In general, fish are darker-coloured on the back than on the underside. As the darker colour blends with the river or pond bottom, fish tend to be less noticeable to an observer from above. Yet when fish feed near the surface their light under-parts blend with the sky, so that they are not too likely to be seen by enemies swimming below.

Perch, pike, and other species that live among weeds are protected by their vertical stripes. An extreme example of camouflage is the "leaf fish" of the Amazon River which is coloured like a dead leaf and has a projection from its lower lip that resembles a leaf stalk. Even its actions reinforce the illusion: in stalking its prey it drifts along like a dead leaf.

How Fish See and Hear

"Goldie winked at me. I saw him!" my exuberant youngster exclaimed one day during a close scrutiny of the aquarium.

He was disappointed when I pointed out that a fish has no eyelids and therefore cannot wink. However, fish do have eyeballs and when one of these is flicked downward you get the impression of a wink. The lack of eyelids also means that whether the fish is awake or asleep, its eyes are wide open.

Fish do not have keen sight. The part of the eye that takes in light is round—whereas in land animals it is flattened. Fish are near-sighted because of the shape of their eye lens.

"Can the fish hear us?" is another challenging thought to children who enjoy talking to their charges at feeding time. It is doubtful that they can, but they do seem to be aware of hand clapping or the sound of tapping on the aquarium walls.

The fish has no outside ear—or even openings where you would expect to find ears. It has other sense organs, however, through which it can get some of the same impressions that we receive through our ears. In fact goldfish, minnows and others learn to react to whistles and certain other sounds at feeding time.

Fish Scales

The scales of a fish look a good deal like the tiles on a roof. Each of the scales grows separately from the skin, but they are set at an angle so that they overlap and form a complete covering for the body. Naturalists sometimes call this scaly covering the "outside skeleton".

Some fish, the catfish for one, do not have scales. Among the species that have, a newly hatched fish of the bony group lacks the protection of scales for its skin; but it does not take long for them to develop. Some kinds of scales—those of the eel, for example—are so tiny that you can hardly notice them.

A curious feature of some members of the tuna family is that they are only partly scale-covered.

TELLING THE AGE OF FISH

As the fish grows, its scales grow too. You can tell the age of many of the bony fish by the markings on their scales; by examining the rings you can tell how many birthdays they have passed. Of course you will not want to do this with your goldfish pet. Its scales should never be touched, let alone pulled out of the skin. A protective slime covers the scales and if this is rubbed off by dry hands or in any other way, death may result for the fish. If it is necessary to move the fish from one container to another home, or to a temporary tank while the aquarium is being cleaned, this should be done with great care.

Children enjoy studying the scales cleaned from a fish destined for the family dinner. Any youngster who knows how to count will get a thrill looking at the scales through a magnifying glass, checking the number and nature of the rings, and reporting the age of the main course for dinner.

"*It Was* That *Big!*"

Among fish, size is not so standardized as among mammals. The goldfish is an outstanding case in point. In an aquarium it remains small, whereas, given the freedom of a pond, it increases its size many times over. Such factors as the temperature and acidity of the water and the type of food available limit the length and weight a fish can attain.

Most of the really big fish are found in the sea—though there is a huge species, the arapaima, that lives in the rivers of Brazil and attains a weight of four hundred pounds. Among the giants of the sea is that popular American food, the tuna. These giants vary in size depending on the regions to which they are native, but a weight of a thousand pounds is about the maximum. Another big fish is the spectacular swordfish. Few sports are as adventurous as deep-sea fishing, and many a boy or girl, thrilled by pictures or films, looks forward to taking a marlin or sailfish with rod and reel. Meanwhile, most of us are content with less exciting fish.

Fish Migrate Too

"What happened to the fish when the water froze?" children often ask as they prepare to go skating over ice that was a rippling lake or stream only a few weeks before.

There is more than one answer to this question. Some fish—the common sucker, for example—burrow in the mud and may be frozen and thawed without being any the worse! Others remain active if the water under the ice is deep enough. As for carp and some other species, they move *en masse* to deeper water at the beginning of winter.

Children accept the seasonal travels of birds rather casually because they can witness some phases of their migrations each year; but they are likely to be surprised to find that many fish migrate too. Even their parents often do not realize how widespread the migration habit is among fish. Except for the fish living in ponds, a great many may make migratory journeys in the course of their lives. Sometimes the individuals in a travelling "school" are counted—or estimated!—by the million.

SPAWNING MIGRATIONS

Apart from the journeys of fish to deeper waters for the winter, some species of fresh-water fish travel many miles in search of food. There are also salt-water migrations by fish that swim away from their feeding grounds to deposit their eggs. A famous example is that of the North Sea herring migrating in the autumn to coastal waters off France. There they spawn and go northward again. When the young hatch they swim to the surface to feed and are gradually swept north by the main currents until they reach the North Sea. There are still other migrations that take fish from the salty ocean to fresh inland waters to deposit their eggs.

How to Keep an Aquarium Successfully

A home aquarium may be a simple matter of keeping one or two goldfish or it may be a full-scale hobby involving a variety of fishes. Tropical and toy fishes are more difficult to raise than the goldfish, but even this hardy pet requires certain favourable conditions in order to survive.

The goldfish needs adequate amounts of water—about a gallon for every inch of fish in the tank. It must be given food in proper amounts; overfeeding is a far more common trouble than insufficient food. The water must be kept clean—yet the fish must not be subjected to a sudden change in temperature when fresh water is provided. The tank must have the right amount of sunlight—not too much, not too little. Several hours of hot summer sun may kill the occupants of a small tank.

Plants are attractive in an aquarium and give the fish a sheltered place to rest and possibly to lay eggs. Contrary to general opinion, they are not essential, however, and too many plants are harmful rather than beneficial.

The popularity of goldfish has put goldfish breeding on a substantial commercial basis. A goldfish hatchery in Maryland, America, covers 150 acres and turns out about five million fish a year!

HOW LONG FISH LIVE

Properly cared for, the common goldfish may reach an age of

twenty-five or thirty years. Many species of fish have a long life span, but in the natural state they are not likely to live to a ripe old age: they have too many enemies, and some—such as the Pacific coast salmon—die after spawning. However, records of fish in ponds or aquariums tell us of catfish that lived sixty years, halibut that reached thirty, and trout that flourished for eighteen years.

Fishes in the Brook

Not long after most children learn the "little fishes in the brook" rhyme, they have a strong desire to join Daddy when he goes to catch fish. There is something about dangling a hook in water and wondering what it may bring up that has a universal appeal for youngsters. If you have access to remote country streams you have a perfect setting for introducing your child to the sport of fishing.

But even without your efforts you may find him tying a bent pin to a string, getting ready to try his luck at a pond in the park. Though fishing may be inconvenient to supervise, it is a hobby well worth encouraging. A five-year old always seems to be letting his cap fall into the pond, with himself on the verge of following the cap. But give him a few more years and the wholesome outdoor sport of fishing is something you and he will be thankful for.

HOW TO PLAN A FISHING TRIP

When you plan a fishing trip you can get helpful information from several sources. The local fishing-tackle dealer may be a mine of information about the fish to be caught in nearby ponds and streams, and in most cases he will be only too happy to put his knowledge at your disposal. Local fishermen will also be helpful once they see you are serious in your intentions. You will want to know what fish are most common, the best places to fish from, the kind of tackle to use and so on.

JOIN AN ANGLING SOCIETY

It has been estimated that there are some four hundred thousand people in England and Wales who make angling their regular hobby. Angling clubs exist by the thousand; there is certain to be one in your locality, and if you find that you like fishing you might well consider joining it. You will get the best possible advice from your fellow-members, and learn a great deal about fishes and their ways just by listening to the talk that goes on when enthusiastic anglers get together.

Do not think that angling is just a matter of catching fish to cook and eat. An enthusiastic angler who wants to know more about the habits of the fish that he catches may be in a position to provide valuable information to scientific workers. Many of the fishes in our national collection at South Kensington were caught by anglers, and there are a surprising number of cases of fish that were new to science being first recognized by anglers who had caught them.

The Carps and the Sticklebacks

THE CARPS HAVE SHARP HEARING

The great order of fishes (Cyprinidae) to which the carps belong also includes many common denizens of our ponds and streams, such as the dace, roach, rudd, tench, minnow and bream. They have one curious characteristic in common. The swim bladder is joined to each ear by a chain of small bones called the Weberian ossicles, so that the swim bladder becomes a sort of underwater microphone. It can pick up sound vibrations in the water and transmit them to the ears, which makes the cyprinid fishes, such as the carp, particularly sensitive to sound.

In the loach the front part of the swim bladder is enclosed in a bony capsule which is in contact with the skin above the pectoral fin by a pair of tubes. We believe that this extraordinary device causes the fish to be sensitive to changes in the pressure of the barometer, so that they can tell when the weather is going to change. In Germany, loaches are called "weather-fishes".

THE PLUCKY STICKLEBACK

Another attractive little resident of brooks in this country is the stickleback. It is perhaps best known for its gameness. The three-spined stickleback (*Gasterosteus aculeatus*) at breeding time is probably the most pugnacious fish of all, in spite of its small size. Rival males engage

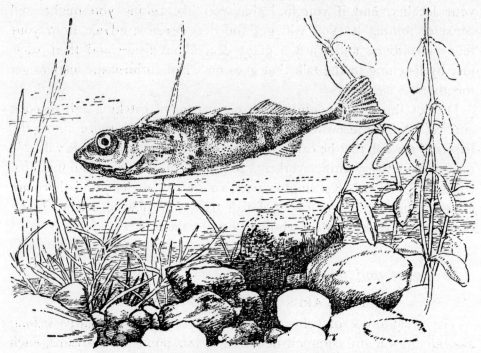

THE STICKLEBACK IS A SCRAPPER

Despite its small size, the stickleback leads a full and adventurous life. Fierce and courageous,
the males fight duels during the courting period. But they also have their tender side,
building nests and guarding the eggs after their fickle mates depart. The male stickleback
looks after his family until they are old enough to swim away.

one another in fierce combat, rushing at one another and endeavouring
to sink their pelvic spines in the flesh of their enemy. After each rush
the combatants retire to shelter in the neighbourhood of their nests,
from which they rush out again when they are ready. The battle is
rather like an encounter between two knights in olden days, and it
usually continues until one contestant has had enough and retires. In
many cases it may even end in the death of one of the combatants, his
belly ripped wide open by the pelvic spines of the other fish.

At the end of the contest the winner takes on an even more resplendent
colour. The loser, if he survives, is for some time bullied by the victor.

Catching Fish for Observation

It is satisfying to catch fish for food or for the sheer fun of it, but
taking them for observation makes an interesting hobby. You need

a barbless hook for this purpose, and the simplest solution is to file the barb off a regular or fly-tied hook. When you catch a fish of the right size, remove it quickly with wet hands and drop it into a wide-mouthed gallon jar of water. You can then study the actions of this underwater creature at leisure.

Another method is to securely cover with wire mesh the top of the jar in which the fish is captive, and place the jar on its side in shallow water with about an inch of air between the water and the top side. Then you can watch the fish for a day or more.

CATCHING FISH WITH A NET

An old and widely used method is taking fish with a net, which you can employ if it is not against the law in your locality. A dark-coloured net, deep and tapering toward a rounded bottom, is best.

This is how to use the net: walk into a shallow pond or stream and hold the net as you would a hoe. Walk slowly, keeping your shadow from falling in front of you and thus frightening the fish away. When you see a fish, twirl the net rapidly in the air so that the opening will cut the water first. Then, with a downward swoop, cover the fish and drag the net briefly shoreward along the bottom. As you lift the net from the water, twist it again so that the opening faces upward; then immediately transfer your catch into a jar or bucket of water.

KEEPING RECORDS OF FISH

Keeping a chart of fish found in your region can be as rewarding as a bird or mammal record. To prepare a chart devoted to fish, you can set up five columns with headings for name and brief description, spawning grounds, feeding grounds, natural food, and bait accepted. You may, if you wish, add columns for the date and place of specimens caught, and another in which a small sketch may be made. Such a chart is fun to keep up and in time becomes a lively textbook for children in learning about native fish.

VISITING FISH HATCHERIES

A trip to a fish hatchery is entertaining and a child can learn a great deal from observing the fish in all stages of development and discovering how streams and lakes are stocked. Most hatcheries have regular visiting hours for the public, and if there is not a hatchery near your home, you may discover one during a holiday trip. In some places roadside signs may direct you to hatcheries, or a travel guidebook may mention them as amongst the local places of interest.

Family Life in the Fish World

Duels between rival males are not the only drama to be observed in the lives of sticklebacks. They belong to the interesting group of fish that make nests for their families.

Before mating the male stickleback chooses a spot for the nest, usually amongst the stems of aquatic plants where the stream is not flowing too swiftly. Then he collects pieces of roots and stems and any other material that he can find and sticks them together to form the nest; he uses a sticky substance that is secreted by his own kidneys. The finished nest is a hollow, barrel-shaped structure. The inside is made smooth by plastering it with a sticky secretion.

The female stickleback, recently won by right of conquest, deposits her eggs in the nest and then takes leave of home and mate. But the male does not share her irresponsibility. He stays close to the nest, bravely defending it from enemies until the eggs hatch. Even then his responsibilities are not over, for he continues to look after the young until they can swim away.

FISH THAT DON'T LAY EGGS

Not all fish lay eggs. Some species, ranging from the great tiger shark to the tiny guppy, give birth to young that are in an advanced state of development. A guppy produces at least twenty-five and perhaps as many as fifty offspring at a time; but the parent fish eat many of their young, and only a small proportion survives.

Some Famous Fish

TROUT—FISHERMAN'S FAVOURITE

Trout live in cool mountain streams or lakes, where they feed on a variety of insects that lay eggs on water; the trout also greedily snatch the emerging insects as they hatch. These feeding habits make fly-fishing for trout an exciting sport as the fisherman lures his victim with imitations of its favourite food. In small streams trout rarely exceed half a pound; but in larger rivers and lakes where food is abundant they often reach from five to ten pounds.

How Trout Build Nests. One female trout lays hundreds of eggs. For her nest she seeks water with a gravelly bottom, perhaps where the brook she inhabits flows into a larger stream. There the mother fish shapes a depression with her tail and carries away larger stones in her mouth.

After she has laid her eggs in the nest and the male has fertilized them, she moves a little upstream and repeats the whole process. The gravel and sand she displaces are carried along by the current. Most of the discarded material is conveniently deposited over the first nest, protecting the eggs it contains. The mother trout makes several nests and lays eggs in all of them before she is finished with the job.

Legal Protection for the Trout. In spite of the enormous quantities of eggs laid by trout, these fish were in serious danger of extermination once motor highways began opening wilderness country to ever-increasing numbers of fishermen. Apart from being destroyed by their natural enemies, such as other fish that eat the eggs and young, the trout were caught by these fishermen who gave no thought to size or season or how many fish might be left in a stream.

The passing of effective conservation laws prevented the disappearance of trout from native waters by regulating the seasons for trout fishing, the number a fisherman may catch and the size a fish must be before it can be taken.

SALMON—THEY LEAP WATERFALLS

Many children have heard about the travels of the salmon, for this fish has become a symbol of determination to reach a goal. Pacific salmon swim hundreds of miles to their spawning grounds in North American rivers; the Atlantic salmon go hundreds of miles to reach theirs in rivers of Europe or of America.

If you had the opportunity to be at a waterfall where salmon were making their way upstream, you might see them putting their noses out of the swirling water as if "sizing up" the situation. They turn their heads against the falling water and twist their bodies like bows, then straighten out again. They bring every muscle into play as they try to progress.

Sometimes they succeed by practically climbing the cascade, at other times they top it with a single leap. No matter what their method, they never give up. If need be, they wait for days—even weeks!—until a change in the volume of water provides a better opportunity to scale the barrier.

Pacific salmon rarely survive spawning to return to the sea. Their usual fate is to die after breeding.

EELS—VERSATILE CREATURES

"Is that a *fish*? Looks like a snake to me!"

With some reason the children are dubious when Daddy displays an eel as the morning's "catch". But despite its elongated, snake-like form it is a true fish, having gills for breathing and fins for swimming.

Eels and Snakes. The well-known figure of speech, "slippery as an eel", makes a good point of contrast between this fish and the snake. The skin of a snake is never slimy; that of an eel is always slimy. The eel's skin is thick and flexible, with the scales lodged in it instead of on the outside. Quantities of tiny glands in the skin produce a sticky mucus. These factors, combined with the creature's suppleness, give it the ability to slip through anyone's fingers.

Eels Love Privacy. Eels live in all kinds of waters, in mountain lakes and streams, in salt-water pools along the shore, and in stagnant ponds. Clean water or foul—it makes no difference to the welfare of these hardy fish. It might seem strange, therefore, that we do not see them more frequently. The fact is, however, that eels are secretive creatures, and much of the time they lie buried in mud. If something seriously disturbs them in their hiding place, they come out in swarms; they live in groups.

Vast Migrations. Like salmon, eels make astounding migratory journeys—but they reverse the salmon's procedure. Instead of leaving the ocean for fresh water, they travel from ponds and lakes down rivers to the depths of the ocean—and there the females eject their eggs.

The two species of eel—one European, the other American—that spawn in the same area in the Atlantic, travel in opposite directions. The young whose parents come from American rivers take about a year to travel from their ocean breeding place to the American continent; the offspring of European species take three years to reach their destination in Europe.

In the course of its travels the eel has a notable advantage over most fish. It has specialized gills that can store a certain amount of water. This makes it possible for the eel to leave a stream or pond and wriggle over land to another body of water some distance away.

A FISH OUT OF WATER

One of the most remarkable oddities of the fish world is the climbing perch, which can survive for several days out of water. Equipped with pectoral fins that are sturdy enough to act as legs, the climbing perch "walks" on land and has even been known to climb low tree trunks.

Fish that are Different

THE FISH THAT WALKS

The fish family has its share of fantastic creatures. In some ways their real-life qualities are more amazing than those of mythological monsters of legend and myth. The climbing perch is the commonest of these believe-it-or-not fish. It can survive out of water for several days, and its pectoral fins are strong enough to support its body by acting as legs! This perch may be said to walk rather than wriggle, and it has been found on low tree trunks.

"FLYING" FISH

Perhaps more generally known than the walking fishes are those that leave the water and glide above its surface. If you travel in tropical waters, such as those around Bermuda or the West Indies, you frequently see some of these gliders in action. Most expert of the group, the "flying fish" travel through the air about three feet above the water at forty miles an hour, and may go as much as four hundred yards at a stretch. All the "flying fish"—they glide rather than fly —live in the sea, with the exception of one little "butterfly" fish of Africa which makes brief excursions over its freshwater home.

SEA HORSES—NATURE'S ECCENTRICS

The sea horse, despite its name, is a fish, and strictly a swimming fish at that; but its method of swimming is amusingly different. Children delight in seeing a group of them in a public aquarium, moving through the water with an appearance of great dignity—head upright, fins at the back. Any onlooker is bound to be convulsed with laughter when the sea horse rolls its eyes; for a sea horse can look straight ahead with one eye and backward with the other at the same time.

But these features by no means exhaust the eccentricities of this odd little fish. (It averages about three inches in length.) The eggs of the sea horse are incubated in a pouch that belongs to the *male*—not the female. The mother sea horse transfers her eggs to the pouch as soon as they are produced; and there they stay until they hatch.

The dried bodies of sea horses are prize discoveries for boys and girls at a beach, where the animals are often stranded by the tide.

THE SEA HORSE—AS ODD AS ITS NAME

The ways of a sea horse are strange indeed. It is a fish—not a horse; but it has a horse-shaped head and a tail that reminds us of a caterpillar's. It swims upright, and its eyes move independently of each other. The eggs of the sea horse are carried in a pouch—by the male! Bony plates cover the body of this fish.

SHOCKING FISH

Another unusual fish you may encounter at the seashore is the little electric star gazer, which spends much of its time buried to its eyes in sand. Only if you happen to step on one is its hiding place quickly revealed: its power to give an electric shock is its means of defence.

There are other fish, larger than the star gazer, that are also equipped with "batteries", but they are not native to our country. One of these is the electric catfish of Africa, another the electric eel of South America which not only uses its powers of shock to defend itself, but also as a weapon for securing food.

Just as zoos give you an opportunity to see strange mammals, so public aquariums present some rare and exotic fishes. A trip to one of these aquariums is the best substitute for a trip underseas.

SHARKS—NOT SO FEROCIOUS

The "ferocious" shark, like the pirates of old who captured the imagination of adventure-loving children, represents a terrible menace of the sea. Any story of shipwreck immediately takes on an element of terror when "shark-infested waters" are mentioned.

Yet it is claimed sometimes that sharks never attack humans but eat only small forms of oceanic life. If you watch native boys fearlessly diving after coins tossed by tourists in the harbour of Nassau in the Bahamas, you may conclude that there is a sound basis for this theory. Frequently the fins of sharks which abound in nearby waters may be seen cutting the surface close by the divers—yet the sharks never molest the boys. The probable explanation is that the noise and excitement and the evident vitality of the divers discourage the sharks.

The "Man-Eater". Actually the biggest member of the shark family, the whale shark, is quite harmless to humans, eating only small fish, jellyfish, and shell creatures. By way of contrast, the great white shark, which is found in all warm seas, comes legitimately by its other name

A CATFISH THAT GIVES A SHOCK

The electric catfish, found in the River Nile and in some other parts of Africa, has been known for centuries, and was even used by the ancients for treating disease or as a love-charm! Much has still to be found out about its diet and mode of life.

of "man-eater". It will devour almost anything it can find, including humans as well as other sharks. The victim need only be disabled or too small to defend itself.

Neighbours of the Fish

WHALES—BIGGEST MAMMALS OF THEM ALL

Whales are the biggest animals in the world. Fully grown, one of them may weigh ten times as much as an elephant! The heroic whale-hunters in the palmy days of Nantucket and New Bedford created one of the imperishable epics of American history when they sailed the seven seas in search of this mighty prey.

The enormous size of the whale is bound to impress a child. He is likely to be even more amazed when he learns that whales are mammals —though they live in water, as fish do. "How is it, then, that they're mammals?" he will surely demand.

Whale "Babies". One proof that whales are mammals is the fact that the babies are born alive and are nourished by their mother's milk. Whale calves are undoubtedly the biggest babies produced by any kind of animal, although their size depends on the size and species of the parent. Occasionally it has been possible to record birth weights, and we have a record of an eighty-foot blue whale that bore a four-ton baby! The whale mother nurses her calf by means of a special compressor muscle that injects into its mouth milk which looks exactly like cow's milk.

Whales Have Hair. Like land-dwelling mammals, whales are warm-blooded; this means that the blood remains at pretty much the same temperature regardless of how warm or cold the animal's surroundings may be. But how about the remaining test of a mammal? Does the whale, with its bare skin, meet the mammal requirement for having fur or hair? Well, it has some hairs—just a few!—sprouting under its chin. Its ancestors of long ago doubtless had a great deal more hair.

How Whales Breathe. But here is another unorthodox feature of the whale. We know that mammals, unlike fish, do not have gills.

How, then, does the whale manage to breathe in its ocean home? Like the land mammals, it must take oxygen into its lungs.

This mammal of the sea has nostrils at the top of its head, making possible a quick intake of air when it comes to the surface. When the whale is below the surface, special muscles close the nostrils firmly against water. There is also a passageway at the back of the mouth which directly connects the nose passage with the windpipe. Thus water cannot reach the whale's lungs even when its mouth is open. Ordinarily a whale comes up for air every few minutes; but it can stay below the surface twenty minutes or more by making use of oxygen stored in its blood.

"There She Blows!" During an ocean voyage you might see the last phase of the whale's unique breathing operation. The exclamation "There she blows!" on shipboard calls attention to one or two fine sprays, looking like steam erupting from the water. They indicate the spot where a whale has just risen to the surface and exhaled! The blast of air sent out of its nostrils is very warm and saturated with water vapour. The blast condenses as it strikes the colder air, forming the columns of spray that have led people to insist—incorrectly—that whales spout water.

How Whales Swim. If you are looking at a picture of a whale that shows its whole body, it will be interesting to see whether your child can notice an important difference between the whale's tail and the tail fin of a fish. The former flattens out into a broad paddle, lying in a horizontal plane. This is just the opposite of the fish's tail, which is always expanded vertically. While the fish helps move itself forward by lashing its tail to the right and left the whale propels itself forward with an up and down motion.

What Whales Eat. After learning the story of Jonah and the whale, a child may ask: "Do whales really eat people?"

Strangely enough, this largest of creatures lives on very small animals. Only one species—the sperm whale—is capable of swallowing a man whole. Others would be apt to choke on any large prey. The sperm whale's teeth are usually only on the lower jaw; its diet consists chiefly of fish and squid.

Of course, the "killer" whales and the species known as porpoises have teeth; but the largest whales are equipped, instead, with enormous strainers. These are made of whalebone plates which, despite their name, are not bone at all but material resembling that of human finger-nails. The whalebone plates, bordered with a horsehair-like fringe, grow from the roof of the mouth. When the whale swims with its

THE SEA COW

The Northern Sea Cow, also called Steller's Sea Cow, after Steller, the naturalist who discovered it on an expedition to Bering Island in 1741. Soon, alas, man had killed them off, and now the term "sea-cow" is applied to two other sirenians—the dugong and the manatee.

mouth open, quantities of shrimps and other small creatures are enmeshed; when the whale closes its mouth, the water is forced out but the victims cannot escape from the trap.

MERMAIDS—GLAMOUR GIRLS OF THE SEA

Fairy tales, cartoons, and sometimes decorative motifs introduce most children to the fantastic, lovely ladies known as mermaids. Many primitive people the world over have legends about mermaids. Babylonian art dating from about 1800 B.C. depicts mermaids, and only a century ago Barnum featured a "stuffed mermaid" in his side show! The inquiring mind of a child plays, naturally enough, with the idea of mermaids—even if "no such animal" is alive now, did it ever exist? If not, why were mermaids "thought up"?

The sea cow, a creature which, like the whale, is a sea-dwelling mammal, probably gave rise to the mermaid legend. The sea cow's head is shaped much like that of the seal; its body is plump but somewhat fishlike. Its startling feature is its face, which suggests an oversize, ugly human. It is believed that when early navigators saw sea cows raise their heads above water, they were struck by the animals' part human, part fishlike appearance. As they did not have binoculars to help them see more clearly, they reported these creatures as glamorous mermaids!

SPONGES

Boys and girls can learn something of life on the floor of tropical seas by examining the natural (not synthetic) sponges. The sponge, when it is alive and growing at the bottom of the sea, looks more like a plant than an animal. There are many varieties of sponges, but not all of them are used commercially as some skeletons are too thin or scratchy or brittle. Sometimes the skeletons become detached and float in on a beach. However, the sponges destined for commercial use are obtained by divers or by workers who pull them from the ocean floor with tongs fastened to long poles.

CORALS—SEMI-PRECIOUS ORNAMENTS

Another sea animal that children may know from its skeleton is the coral. As in the case of sponges, there are many varieties of corals. Apart from the type used for making necklaces and ornaments, there are the reef-building, "stony" kind. These are responsible for the well-known coral isles of the Pacific, as well as the great coral reefs such as may be found near the Bahamas and off the coast of Australia. The Great Barrier Reef off Australia is more than a thousand miles long and has caused many a shipwreck.

Architect of the Seas. Any child's imagination is bound to be stimulated by the amazing explanation of how the tiny soft-bodied coral polyp produces these gigantic structures. A newborn coral polyp is active at first and swims freely; but soon it fastens itself to a rock or to the sea floor. Using carbonate of lime obtained from food and water, it forms a little platform under its body and a hard wall (called the skeleton) around itself.

What happens to most kinds of corals is that these new polyps remain attached to the parent and in turn produce new buds. As the older ones die, young polyps build on top of their skeletons and thus the structure grows until an island or reef is formed.

THE BASHFUL SNAILS

Observing a snail's daily activities need not be the only pleasure your child derives from his unusual pet. He can also train the animal to be less shy. I knew one friendly snail that would come out of its shell when summoned by a sharp clicking sound, and would proceed to eat from its owner's fingers.

When a snail has enough confidence to come out of its shell, your child will be able to observe its eyes, which are located at the ends of tentacles attached to its head; he can also study the horny jaws that cut up the plant material it eats. If the snail learns to eat from his finger, he can feel the tiny teeth on the tongue which give it a sandpaper texture.

How to Take Care of a Pet Snail. A glass terrarium furnished with moss and ferns makes an excellent home for a snail. You will need a wire covering for the enclosure, as snails can crawl up anything— even a slippery piece of glass. They owe this ability to a substance they secrete as they travel. Snails require little food, usually thriving on cabbage or lettuce leaves, carrot pulp and the like.

At the Seashore

If you could take your child on an exploring trip around a coral reef, you would find many fantastic forms of life such as the giant plantlike sea anemones, and such shellfish as the bright pink crab that camouflages itself with bits of sponge. Such an expedition is out of the question for most of us, so it is fortunate that a number of these

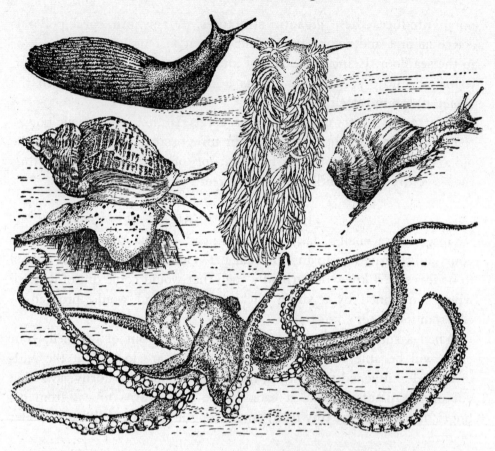

ALL MOLLUSCS—YET HOW DIFFERENT!

Most molluscs—but not all of them—have a shell and a foot or its equivalent for getting about. The number of different molluscs is over 70,000. Top left: black garden slug, and, below it, whelk. Top centre: sea slug. Top right: garden snail. Bottom: octopus.

tropical wonders can be seen much closer to home—in tide pools along the shore, and on rocky coasts and sandy beaches.

Looking for these creatures and learning something of their way of life can become a delightful summer hobby. You will find that a magnifying hand lens is a valuable piece of equipment to help the youngster enjoy his discoveries to the fullest. Children of six or over can use a microscope to good advantage.

STINGING HYDROIDS

You can often come across hydroids as you examine a tide pool. These are tiny creatures that—like the giant sea anemones of the coral reefs—resemble flowers. When they are magnified, the hydroids are revealed as animals. Like the corals, they are known as polyps. Each individual is attached to a delicate stalk, and it has numerous thread-like tentacles that are equipped with stinging cells. Small creatures that come close are paralysed and drawn into the opening that serves the hydroid as a mouth. Many hydroids are quite transparent, and for this reason they are especially interesting to observe.

FLOWER-LIKE SEA ANEMONES

In the tide pools, too, you may find sea anemones, much smaller than those of tropical seas yet larger than the hydroids. When undisturbed, they expand into flower-like forms; but they can contract quickly into an unattractive jelly-like mass. When they are in this form you will note their resemblance to jellyfish; actually the two animals are closely related.

Shellfish—They Aren't Really Fish

A child running barefoot along the seashore is likely to have an unpleasant encounter with these creatures, for their sharp edges can inflict painful cuts. He soon learns to watch out for mussels, clams, and all shellfish that are exposed to view during low tide. He will surely wonder, too, how these animals can be fish when they are so different from salmon, trout, or other "regular" fish.

The fact is that the term "shellfish", though constantly used, is incorrect; the proper name for these animals is "molluscs". Every king of mollusc—there are something like seventy thousand species!—has a soft body enveloped in a mantle which in most cases manufactures or secretes a hard shell. There are two siphons in the mantle; one of them brings water to the animal, the other carries the water away after it has passed through the gills.

The mollusc's shell is sometimes described as a skeleton—a skeleton without a backbone. Instead of being an internal structure, the skeleton is carried on the outside of the body.

THE CLAM'S PEARLY LINING

One of the best-known molluscs, the clam, has a shell made up of three layers—a thin one on the outside, a thick strong middle layer, and a smooth pearly lining. When a bit of sand or other foreign matter gets lodged within the shells, it becomes coated like the lining and in time may become a true pearl.

SQUATTERS' RIGHTS

We find molluscs not only in the sea, but in freshwater lakes and streams and on land as well. Some of them—the periwinkle, for example —have a single shell; others, such as clams and oysters, have two shells hinged along the back. Shellfish give the deceptive appearance of leading a peaceful existence, though the fact is that life is a constant struggle for them.

They are devoured by a variety of animals, and they often vie with each other for living space.

Oysters settle as a rule in fairly deep water, though sometimes a colony is located on a mudflat that is exposed to the air during low tide.

In such a situation you may see an invasion taking place. Mussels, which multiply with a great rapidity, may move in and smother the oysters out of existence by sheer weight of numbers. But, once the mussel colony is established, it may in turn be invaded by a host of barnacles which soon take over the territory for their own.

One of the molluscs' worst enemies is an innocent-looking snail with the sinister name of oyster drill. It plays great havoc in oyster beds, boring holes through the oyster shell and feeding on the soft underlying flesh.

THE SELF-EFFACING CRABS

You have to keep a sharp lookout to catch a glimpse of these notable creatures of the seashore. Some are expert at disguising themselves by putting seaweed or bits of sponge on their back; some hide themselves almost completely in the sand as they lie in wait for prey; and some are very small.

The Rock Crab. It should not be too difficult to discover the rock crab, which is common on most rocky shores. Full grown, it is a little over five inches wide, and is commonly reddish purple in colour. Like all crabs, the little fellow has five pairs of legs. The first pair are

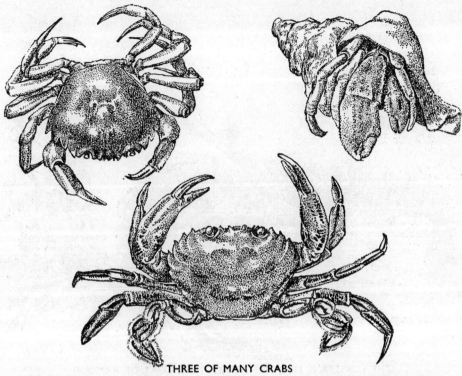

THREE OF MANY CRABS

Shown here are, top left, common rock crab; top right, hermit crab; below, velvet swimming crab. The hermit crab lacks a hard protective shell, so it finds empty mollusc shells in which to live, often changing its abode. Not all the crabs spend their lives in the sea.

adapted as pinching claws, and in some crabs the last two pairs, shaped like fins, serve effectively as swimming aids.

It is amusing to watch crabs walk—they move sideways instead of forwards or backwards. Shore crabs are rather slow in their movements; the swimming crabs are considerably more active.

Spare Parts. If a crab accidentally loses a claw, it can grow a new one. During its lifetime it also replaces its shell, not because of a mishap, but because its body gradually grows too big for the shell. When the original shell starts getting too tight, the animal pulls itself free, and until it grows a new covering it is known as a "soft-shell" crab.

THE AGGRESSIVE LOBSTERS

If you make a habit of observing the activity among the seaweed in shallow waters, you may have an opportunity to see a struggle

THE LOBSTER IS HELPLESS WITHOUT ITS COAT OF ARMOUR
Though the lobster has a great fighting asset in its brutal claws, its tough shell has enormous defensive value. At the times when the lobster has to shed its shell for a new one, it is helpless against the onslaught of its enemies. The lobster is valuable as food.

between a lobster and a crab, although such encounters are rather infrequent. The crab—even a large one—apparently has little chance against his opponent: a lobster's claws are extremely powerful. One of them is very broad and is used for crushing; the narrower one cuts food to bits. Its mouth can crush as well as bite. It is also probable that the lobster has an advantage over the crab because its feelers, especially a second pair, are longer than the crab's. With them the lobster can investigate holes and crevices and is extra-sensitive to danger as well as possible prey.

Shell Hobbies are Fun

SHELL COLLECTING

Sea shells delight children who live inland as well as those who have the seashore close at hand. They may collect them—as stamps

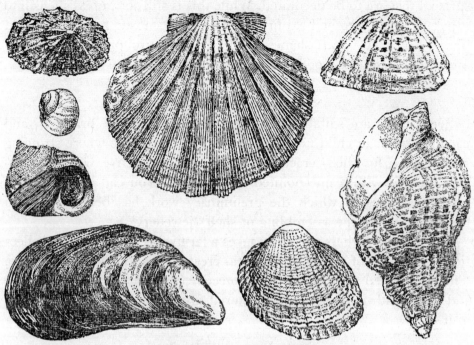

WONDERFUL IN THEIR VARIETY

Shells of an almost endless diversity of shape, colour and size are truly amongst the wonders of Nature. Here are a few well-known ones. Left from top: limpet, necklace shell, periwinkle, common mussel. Right, common limpet and (below) common whelk. Centre, top, scallop and (below) common cockle, still a popular dish in many parts of Britain.

and coins are collected through purchase at stores, by order from catalogues, and through trading with correspondents the world over.

Shells have a multiple appeal. Some, such as the giant conch shell, intensify the sounds they pick up in their spiral interior and thus bring to a child's ear "the sound of the sea".

DECORATIVE USES FOR SHELLS

Shells have a further appeal because you can make art objects with them. If your child is an enthusiastic collector, he may call on you for ideas to put quantities of shells to use.

One project that serves the purpose is making shell book-ends. You start these with two triangular blocks of wood, each attached to a heavy wood base about six inches square. Then you apply a coat of ready-mixed putty, nearly a quarter of an inch thick, to the outer surfaces that are to be decorated. While this is still soft, press shells into it just far enough to be held firmly. With good cutting tools your wood blocks may take varied shapes, while the shell groupings and designs are limitless and the wood and putty may be painted as desired.

SHELL HANDICRAFTS

Some shells are suitable for making belts, necklaces, bracelets, and earrings. A small child needs help in making the holes where stringing is necessary, for shells crack easily. The most effective way to puncture them is with a fine-pointed electric drill. You can buy shellcraft hobby packages in which the preliminary work has been done; this greatly simplifies the assembling of shell "jewellery".

A child who gathers sea shells takes a far livelier interest in his collection if he thinks of a shell as a fortress created by a soft-bodied creature. The shell served the mollusc as a protective covering during its lifetime, and after death remained as a memorial to the little creature that lived in it.